GREAT EVENTS
IN THE LIFE OF
ABRAHAM LINCOLN

5 *Becomes President of the United States, March 4, 1861*

6 *Hears about the fall of Fort Sumter, which starts the Civil War, 1861*

8 *Delivers his Gettysburg Address, 1863*

7 *Issues the Emancipation Proclamation, 1862*

Farrow's
Watervi...

D1213765

THE STORY OF
Abraham Lincoln

"He wanted to learn, to know, to live, to reach out; he wanted to satisfy hungers and thirsts he couldn't tell about, this big boy of the backwoods. And some of what he wanted so much, so deep down, seemed to be in the books."

—CARL SANDBURG

*He could split more rails in a day than
anyone in the neighborhood*

THE STORY OF
Abraham Lincoln

By NINA BROWN BAKER

Illustrated by WARREN BAUMGARTNER

ENID LAMONTE MEADOWCROFT
Supervising Editor

PUBLISHERS Grosset & Dunlap NEW YORK

For
BILLY BENNETT

Contents

[*vii*]

Contents

Illustrations

ILLUSTRATIONS

THE STORY OF
Abraham Lincoln

The wagon bumped through the woods

CHAPTER ONE

Good-by, Kentucky!

I THOUGHT we'd build us a boat," little
Abe said. "Pappy went in a boat. Why can't we
go that-a-way? Horseback riding's no fun. You
can ride horseback any day."

Cousin Dennis laughed. "It ain't 'any' day
you can ride horseback all the way to Indianny, Abe. I wish I was a-going! I wouldn't
care how I got there."

As he spoke, Dennis wiggled his toes in the
cool spring water. The two boys had been gathering blackberries. They were tired and hot.
Now they were resting by the spring and cool-
ing their bare feet.

[3]

"Well, Pappy went in a boat," Abe persisted. "I don't see why we can't go the same way Pappy did."

"I'll tell you why," the big boy said.

That was the nice thing about Cousin Dennis, Abe thought. He never told you to hush up when you asked a question. Even though he was sixteen, he'd take time to explain things to a little fellow.

"Your pappy had to go by water," Dennis went on. "He was taking his carpenter tools. And the plow, and some axes and hoes. Then there was them ten barrels of whiskey, too. There wasn't no other way he could get all that stuff to Indianny."

"I wondered about the whiskey," Abe said. "What'd he take all them barrels for? Pappy ain't a drinking man."

"Course not," Dennis agreed. "He took it to trade, Abe. Kentucky whiskey's as good as money over in Indianny. Your pappy can trade his whiskey for food till he's had time to grow some crops."

[4]

"I never thought of that," Abe said. "Pappy's smart, ain't he? But I still don't see why we can't go in a boat, Dennis."

Dennis laughed. "Then you're not as smart as your pappy, Abe. It's a long way by boat. Your pappy floated down Rolling Fork into the Ohio River. Then down the Ohio to Thompson's Ferry in Indianny. That's a mighty long trip. It took him nigh on a month. He come back afoot, striking straight overland. He walked it in a week. Now do you see why he's taking you folks overland?"

"I reckon so," Abe answered. "Pappy's in a hurry to get the new farm cleared before winter. He says it's a right pretty piece of land. Lots of big walnut trees on it. He can make walnut furniture for the settlers. Pappy likes carpentering better than farming, anyhow."

"Yes, I know he does," Dennis said. "But you'll need to raise your own corn and hogs, and a few cows. Well, I guess we better be getting back, Abe. Your mammy wants these berries for supper."

[5]

They made their way back to the Lincoln cabin. It was a poor place on poor land. This part of Kentucky was just about worked out, everyone said. The Lincolns and their neighbors had been hearing about new land in Indiana. A man could get farmland over there very cheaply.

While his neighbors had talked, Abe's father had acted. Tom Lincoln had gone to Indiana and picked out a place to settle. The neighbors could do as they liked. The Lincolns were leaving Kentucky for good.

When the boys reached the log cabin, Abe's sister Sally was setting the table under the big hickory trees. The family usually ate outdoors in summertime.

"I hope you picked plenty of berries," Sally said anxiously. "We got company for supper. Your folks are here, Dennis."

"Yes, Auntie said they'd be over," Dennis answered. "Where are they?"

"Uncle Thomas is down at the barn with

Pappy," the girl replied. "Aunt Betsy and Mammy are inside. No, here they come now. Let me help you, Mammy. That pot's too heavy for you."

Sally took the pot of boiled pork and turnip greens from her mother and set it on the table.

"Go call the menfolks, Abe," she ordered. Sally was only nine but she liked to give orders.

Aunt Betsy Sparrow bustled out of the kitchen with a pan of cornbread. She was a spry old lady with a warm heart. Aunt Betsy had raised Nancy Hanks Lincoln, Abe's mother. Now she was raising young Dennis Hanks, her great-nephew.

In many ways she was doing the same for Abe and Sally. Their mother was a frail young woman who was often ill. The Lincoln children adored Mammy. But it was Aunt Betsy who made them wash their necks and mind their manners.

Abe came back with his father and great-uncle. Briskly Aunt Betsy herded them all to

[7]

the table. "You men can talk while you eat," she scolded. "No sense letting good vittles get cold while you gab about Indianny."

Throughout the meal they talked of nothing else. Thomas Sparrow was like his wife, old but full of life. He listened eagerly to Tom Lincoln's description of Indiana.

To hear Tom tell it, the new state was the Promised Land. A man wouldn't have to scratch for a living there, the way he did in Kentucky. He wouldn't even need to raise hogs for meat. There was wild game enough in Indiana to feed the nation. Bear meat, venison, wild turkey—what more could you want?

Uncle Thomas was a keen hunter.

"By jingo, I got a good mind to go with you!" he exclaimed.

Aunt Betsy snorted. "Not if I know it, Thomas Sparrow! We'll stay where we are." She turned to Abe's father. "Are you aiming to get off tomorrow, Tom?" she asked.

Mr. Lincoln nodded. "Can't see why not.

[8]

There's nothing to keep us here. I've sold the place. Yep, reckon we'll light out tomorrow morning."

Mrs. Lincoln looked up. "Will you take good care of my little rocker, Auntie? I wish I could take it along. Seems like it just fits my back. But Mr. Lincoln says it's too bunglesome to tie on a horse."

"Now don't you worry about your rocker, girl," Tom Lincoln said. "I'll make you a better one soon's we get settled. There ain't no sense carting furniture all that way, even if we could. Let the old folks have what's here. I'll make us a new set out of the finest walnut wood you ever see."

"You mind you do that, Tom," Aunt Betsy said sharply. "Nancy needs some comfort, delicate like she is. And remember she's got to ride all the way on this trip. It's all right for you and the young'uns to foot it. But Nancy ain't got the strength for it."

"Course not," Tom Lincoln agreed. "I'm

[9]

a-putting her sidesaddle on Little Red. He can carry our clothes, too. We'll load the other horse with bedclothes and the pots and skillets. Sally can ride on top if she gets real tired. But us men'll make it on our own feet, won't we, Abe?"

He smiled at his seven-year-old son, and Abe smiled back. "Us men!" How he liked the sound of that! He was still sorry they were not going by boat. But any way you traveled, going to Indianny would be fun.

They started early the next morning. The two loaded horses went at a slow walking pace. At night the family rested in wayside cabins, where kindly Kentucky farmers made them welcome.

On the fourteenth day of their journey they came to the wide Ohio River. Tom Lincoln pointed to the far shore. "That's Indianny," he told them.

They crossed the river by ferry. This was the spot where Mr. Lincoln's flatboat journey had ended. He had left his goods in the care of an Indiana farmer named Posey. Now he made straight for the Posey house.

The tools and the barrels of whiskey were waiting for him. Mr. Posey very kindly offered to lend him a wagon to carry them to the land which Tom Lincoln had chosen for his new farm. The two horses were hitched to the wagon and the goods were loaded in.

Mr. Lincoln helped his wife up to the high wagon seat. He took his place beside her. Sally perched on top of the load. "Come on, Abe," she called. "What are you a-staring at?"

The little boy was standing barefoot in the dusty road. His face had a puzzled look.

"I thought Indianny would be different," he said. "It looks just like where we come from. I mean—well, it's trees, and grass, and just plain old ground. What's different about it?"

"Silly, it's a different *state*," Sally answered. "Look over there across the river. That's Kentucky, where we come from. Here where we

[*11*]

are is Indianny. Kentucky's a state. Indianny's a state. They're *different* states, don't you see?"

"No, I don't," Abe said stubbornly. He looked at the Kentucky shore. He looked around him at Indiana. "They don't look no different to me. This state business is just something somebody made up. You can see a river, or a hill. You can't see a state nohow. It's all just land. What's the sense calling it something you can't see?"

"Abraham!" It was his mother's soft voice. "You're keeping us waiting, son. What are you doing? Saying good-by to Kentucky?"

"I reckon so," Abe replied. He turned and jumped up beside his sister. "I still think this state business is a lot of foolishness," he told her. "Looks to me like it's all the same land, whatever you call it."

CHAPTER TWO

The Half-faced Camp

IT WAS sixteen miles from the river to the new farmland. There was no road. The wagon bumped through the woods. Often Tom Lincoln had to stop the horses and chop a path through the thick brush. The Lincolns camped in the woods the first night. Late on the next afternoon they came to the bank of Little Pigeon Creek.

The tiny stream ran between steep mud banks. Mrs. Lincoln asked anxiously, "How are we going to get across, Mr. Lincoln? I don't see no ford."

Tom Lincoln grinned. "Won't need no

ford, Nancy. We ain't a-crossing. We're here. Jump down and look around you. This is my claim."

"How can you tell, Pappy?" asked Sally. She climbed out of the wagon and looked around her. "It's just like all the woods we passed."

"There's a girl for you!" Abe said scornfully. "Pappy can tell by the axe marks on the trees. He done that when he was here before. Didn't you, Pappy?"

"Yes, and I piled up that heap of brush there," Tom Lincoln said. "Oh, it's the place, all right. A right nice little clearing, with water close by. I couldn't have done better. Well, wife, what do you think of it?"

Mrs. Lincoln was out of the wagon now. She was tired and stiff from the long jolting ride. She looked around her.

It was a beautiful spot. Tall walnut and maple trees stood back from an open space which was covered with thick, short grass. It was a fine place for a cabin. Of course, there

[*14*]

was no cabin yet. The Lincolns would have no home until they built one for themselves.

"I reckon it'll do," the mother said wearily. "I'm so tired I can't see straight. I'll have to rest a spell before I get supper."

"You set down here on the grass, Mammy," Sally said. "I'll tend to the supper. Abe, you get me some wood for a fire."

"I was a-fixing to help Pappy with the horses," Abe answered. "We got to get them unhitched and watered, Sis. Horses come before people, don't they, Pappy?"

"They don't come before your mammy," Tom Lincoln said. "I'll take care of the horses. You go on and build a fire for your sister. Then get the bearskins out of the wagon and rustle up some branches. We'll get Mammy to bed right after we eat. She's plumb wore out."

The children bustled around the campfire. Soon Sally had the simple meal ready. It was fried bacon and hominy, washed down with water from the creek.

The creek water was muddy, with a horrid taste. But Tom Lincoln told the children that he had found a spring not far from the clearing. After they got settled, they could carry their drinking water from the spring.

When supper was over, Abe and his father piled up leafy branches for beds. Covered with bearskins, they made a soft resting place. The

Lincoln family was asleep before the first stars came out.

The next morning Abe could hardly wait till breakfast was over. "Let's start building our house, Pappy," he urged. "I'll help you cut down the trees."

Tom Lincoln shook his head. "It ain't that easy, sonny. Takes a long time to cut logs and build a sound cabin. No, we'll just run us up a half-faced camp. That'll have to do us for a spell."

"All right, then let's start the half-faced camp," Abe said. "What do we do first?"

"Mammy and I will help too," Sally said. "Show us what to do, Pappy."

"Reckon I'll need all hands, and that's the truth," Tom Lincoln agreed. "Come over here, all of you."

He led the family to a spot near the edge of the wood. Two tall trees grew about fourteen feet apart.

"These trees will do," Mr. Lincoln said. "I'll

chop off their lower branches. They'll make two corners of the camp. Then I'll drive two poles in the ground for the other corners."

"How about the walls?" Abe asked.

"I'll show you." Tom Lincoln took out his big jackknife. He cut a long piece of wild grapevine. "We'll twist vines between the poles. Lots of 'em, from the ground up. That'll make a kind of a lattice.

"We'll do the same way for the roof. Then we'll stuff them up with branches and grass and a few logs. If we get enough grass on the roof, it'll keep out the rain just fine. We'll stick it all up with mud from the creek, too, so the grass won't blow away."

With everyone working hard, the camp was finished in a few days. It did not need doors or windows, for there were only three walls.

"That's why they call it half-faced," Mr. Lincoln explained. "We leave the south side open to let in sun and light."

"That's fine now," Sally objected. "But

"That's why they call it half-faced,"
Mr. Lincoln explained

seems to me it'll let in the cold, when winter comes."

"Oh, we'll fix that," said her father. "Come cold weather, we'll build a big log fire just outside the open wall. Keep it going day and night. That'll warm up the camp just fine."

He looked at his wife. "It ain't much of a shelter, I know. But it's the best we can do till spring. It'll take me all winter to cut and trim logs for a regular cabin."

"I'll help you do that," Abe said eagerly. "I'm getting real good with the little axe, Pappy. Course, I can't cut down trees yet. But I can trim off all the branches."

The Lincolns lived in the half-faced camp all winter. Every day Abe went with his father into the woods. The pile of trimmed logs grew steadily. By the time spring came they were ready to build the new cabin.

The building went slowly, for help was scarce. New families were coming into the neighborhood. Far up the creek a mill had been built. Sometimes a friendly neighbor would give Tom Lincoln a hand. But most of the men were busy building their own cabins. The Lincoln home was built almost entirely by Mr. Lincoln and his children.

At last it was done. It had no floor, and very little furniture. Mr. Lincoln never did get around to building the set of walnut furniture he had promised. He found time only to knock together a big table and a few three-legged stools. With the house done, he had to clear his land and plant his crops. Furniture must wait.

One sunny fall day, Abe sat alone on the doorstep. Mrs. Lincoln and Sally were in the woods gathering wild grapes. Tom Lincoln was at a neighbor's house, seven miles away.

Young Abe was busy. He was working on the hide of a raccoon his father had shot. Patiently he scraped the skin with a dull knife. Mammy had said if he got the hide ready she'd make him a coonskin cap.

The boy was working hard and whistling to himself as he worked. He did not even hear a wagon roll into the clearing. He looked up in amazement at a shout. He rubbed his eyes. It couldn't be! But it was!

Abe jumped up, dropping his coonskin. "Cousin Dennis!" he yelled.

CHAPTER THREE

"I Won't Ever Leave You"

ABE dashed wildly across the clearing. There was a wagon drawn by oxen and heaped with household goods. Uncle Thomas and Aunt Betsy Sparrow beamed down at him from the high seat. And standing at the head of the ox team was Cousin Dennis.

"Thought we'd surprise you," Dennis grinned. "Well, ain't you glad to see us?"

"Reckon I am!" Abe said joyfully. "Hey, Dennis, how'd you all get here? Are you a-going to stay?"

"Maybe yes, maybe no," Aunt Betsy said briskly. "Help me down off this seat, Abe—if

[23]

you *are* Abe. Land sakes, you sure have growed, sonny. You don't look nothing like the skinny fellow I remember."

"Oh, I'm Abe, all right, Auntie," Abe said. He gave her a smacking kiss as he helped her down. "Say, this is the best thing that's happened in a coon's age. But I don't know yet how it happened."

"It was your uncle Thomas who made us come," Aunt Betsy said. "Seemed like he just couldn't get his mind off that hunting your pa talked about. Him and Dennis, they didn't give me no peace. 'Indianny, Indianny,' was all I heard from morning till night. Well, I ain't saying I wasn't pining for you young'uns, and for your mammy. How is she, Abe?"

"She's pretty good, Auntie." The boy's face clouded. "She works too hard, though. And sometimes she gets right sick. Me and Sally try to spare her all we can. Mammy'll be awful glad to see you folks."

"I reckon," the old lady agreed. "Thomas, you and Dennis tend to the oxen. I'll go on up to the house. My, Abe, that's a right good-looking cabin. But where's all the folks?"

"Mammy and Sis are hunting for wild grapes," Abe said. "I'll get them. You go on in and set down. Pappy won't be back till supper-time."

Abe ran off into the woods. At his news, his

mother and sister hurried back to the clearing. Aunt Betsy gathered them into her motherly arms.

Nancy Lincoln was so happy that she burst into tears.

"It's been so long, Auntie, so long!" she sobbed. "You'll stay with us, won't you? I just don't see how I can do without you."

"There, there, lamb." The old woman smoothed Nancy's thick dark hair. "I declare I don't know what Tom Lincoln was a-thinking of, to bring you way off here from your own folks. You're looking awful peaked too, girl. You wasn't this thin when you left Kentucky. Well, it's all right now. Aunt Betsy is here to take care of you."

Cousin Dennis looked at Abe and winked. Quietly the two boys stole out of the cabin.

"It's all settled," Dennis said cheerfully. "If Auntie thinks your ma needs her, she'll never go back. That's a load off my mind. She kept telling us not to set our hearts on staying here.

If she didn't like it, we was going to visit a
spell and then go on home. But she'll like it
all right, with Aunt Nancy to baby."

"Mammy needs a little babying," Abe said.
"She don't complain, but she's ailing a lot,
Dennis. I'm sure enough glad Aunt Betsy's
come. And I'm glad you come too," he added
sincerely.

"Thanks. I was waiting for that," Dennis
said with a laugh. "Well, show me around.
You got a good house—bigger than the one
you had on Knob Creek. Why, it's even got a
loft."

"Yes, Pappy said we'd do it right," Abe answered. "I sleep up in the loft, along with the
hams and sacks of corn. It's a heap better sleep-
ing than what I had last winter. You know we
just been in the new cabin a few weeks. We
ain't hardly got used to it yet."

"Where did you live before?" Dennis asked.

"I'll show you." Abe led the way to the half-
faced camp. "We figure on using it for a cow-

"Auntie, you brought my rocker!" she exclaimed

shed, when we get a cow. But we all lived here before we got the cabin built."

Dennis was examining the camp when they heard Sally's voice calling. "Boys! Fetch me some water from the spring. I got to get supper started."

They went back to the house for a pail. Uncle Thomas was busy unloading the wagon. Now, with a proud smile, he brought in Mrs. Lincoln's little rocking chair.

Her pale face lighted with joy. "Auntie, you brought my little rocker! Now it's like it says in the Bible, 'My cup runneth over.' Oh, Auntie, you're so good. Promise you won't never leave me again."

"I won't ever leave you, my dearie," the old woman said tenderly. "You just set and rock awhile. I must say Tom Lincoln's not done much for you in the way of furniture. All talk and no do, that man of yours. Well, never mind. Take it easy now, my lamb. Me and Sally will get supper. Find me an apron, Sal, and let's get a-going."

Tom Lincoln came in a little later. The group around the supper table was a merry one. Tom was sure that the Sparrows could find good land near by. "And while you're a-looking, you'll stay here with us," he said.

"Well, we ain't aiming to put you young folks out," Aunt Betsy answered. "You got a nice cabin here, Tom, but it's pretty small for two families. Maybe we could run us up some kind of a shack for the time being."

"There's the half-faced camp," Abe put in. "It's empty now, Pappy. Couldn't the folks live in that till they get land and build their own house?"

"Sure enough," Tom Lincoln approved. "If you'd rather be by yourselves, the camp's the place for you."

"Where's this camp at?" Aunt Betsy demanded. "I got to be where I'm close to Nancy. There's a heap of work I can take off her hands."

They showed her the half-faced camp and

she said it would do. That night Aunt Betsy
and Uncle Thomas moved in. Most of the fur-
niture they had brought went into the Lincoln
cabin. Most of the housework was done by
Aunt Betsy's tireless old hands. Even after
Uncle Thomas had located his claim, Aunt
Betsy refused to leave the half-faced camp.
Nancy needed her close, she said.

Uncle Thomas and Aunt Betsy Sparrow
lived in the camp for exactly one year. Then
they both were taken ill with "milksick." This
was a strange disease that swept the whole
countryside. It killed horses and cattle as well
as human beings.

There were no doctors in the backwoods
settlement. The Lincolns nursed the Sparrows
as best they could, dosing them with home-
made herb remedies. It was no use. The old
people died within a few days of each other.
Abe helped his father build their coffins.

In that dreary autumn there were many
deaths among the settlers. Before the first snow

fell, the dreaded "milksick" moved into the Lincoln cabin. Frail, gentle Nancy Lincoln had no strength to fight it. Red-eyed from weeping, Tom Lincoln cut down a walnut

tree. He smoothed the satiny wood into sturdy planks to make another coffin. Heartbroken, little Abe whittled wooden pegs to hold it together.

"I WON'T EVER LEAVE YOU"

"All that I am, or ever hope to be," President Lincoln said many years later, "I owe to my angel mother." Abraham Lincoln's mother went home to the angels before her son was ten years old.

CHAPTER FOUR

The New Mother

THE LINCOLN children had a hard time after their mother's death. Twelve-year-old Sally struggled with the cooking, the soapmaking, the washing and cleaning. She did not do very well at it. The work had been enough to keep both Mammy and Aunt Betsy busy. It was too much for one young girl.

Abe and Cousin Dennis helped her all they could. But they had their own work to do. Dennis Hanks was eighteen now. He could swing an axe or guide a plow as well as Tom Lincoln could. Young Abe tried to do everything that Dennis did. He was unusually strong for his age, and he would never admit that any job was too big for him.

The year after his wife's death, Mr. Lincoln went back to Kentucky alone. He was very mysterious about the trip.

"I got some business to tend to back there," he told the children. "I won't stay longer than I have to. You young'uns mind Cousin Dennis and behave yourselves while I'm gone."

He set out on foot. Winter came and he did not return. Abe and Sally were lonely without him. The weeks dragged by slowly.

One cold morning Abe and his sister were huddled close to the fireplace. Cousin Dennis was out helping a neighbor build his barn.

Sally was trying to make her brother some buckskin moccasins. It had looked so easy when Mammy did it! But the needle would hardly go through the tough hide. It stuck Sally's fingers and made them bleed.

"Wish we never had any old winter," she

[35]

said crossly. "Then we could go barefoot all the time. Stick out your foot, Abe."

She slipped the half-finished shoe over his bare, dirty foot.

"Mammy never tried them on every minute," Abe complained. "That don't look much like a shoe to me, Sal. It's more like a buckskin sack."

"Oh, I know it's no good." Tears gathered in Sally's eyes. "I must have cut it wrong somehow. I'll take another piece of skin and try again. Give me—wait! What's that noise outside?"

"I'll see." Abe jumped up and ran to the door.

"Hey, Sis, come and look!" he shouted. "It's the biggest wagon I ever see in my life. There's four horses a-pulling it. Must be some new settlers that lost their way. Reckon they're rich folks, too. Look at all the stuff piled up behind."

Staring, the two children stood in the door-

[*36*]

way. The wagon with its four stout horses came straight toward them.

"Why, that's Pappy a-driving!" Sally exclaimed. "But where in the world did he get that rig? And who are all them folks with him?"

She was soon to know. Tom Lincoln stopped the horses and jumped down from the wagon seat. Then he turned to help the woman who had been sitting beside him. A boy about Abe's age jumped from the wagon, and then two girls. One was almost grown up. The other looked about four years old.

Mr. Lincoln led the woman to where Abe and his sister stood staring.

"These are my young'uns, Sarah," Tom Lincoln said. "Abe and Sally, say howdy to your new mammy."

They were too surprised to speak. But the new Mrs. Lincoln did not wait for words. She was a big, rosy-cheeked woman with kind bright eyes. She smiled warmly at the puzzled children.

[37]

Abe and his sister stood staring

"Reckon your pa didn't tell you he was a-fixing to marry again," she said. "Well, now, we'll get along fine. My children lost their father, and you all lost your mammy. It's just good sense for us to get together. Maybe you've heard that stepmothers are always mean. It ain't so. You'll be just the same to me as my own. Johnny, Sairey, Tildy—come and get acquainted with your new brother and sister."

The two groups of children looked at each other. The young Johnstons were nicely dressed, in clean, warm winter clothing. Abe and his sister looked ragged and neglected. No one said a word.

"Looks like the cat's got everybody's tongue," the new mother said briskly. "Never mind. Young'uns are always bashful at first. You, sonny—Abraham, ain't it? You help Johnny and Pappy get the load off the wagon. Me and the girls will go on inside."

Sarah Johnston Lincoln stood in the one-room cabin and looked around her. The floor

[*39*]

was of earth. The beds were made of posts driven into the ground, supporting corn-husk mattresses. Aunt Betsy's worn-out furniture had mostly fallen to pieces. There was a broken-down chair or two, and a little clothes chest. Mammy's maple rocker still stood by the fireplace. For the rest, there were only the three-legged stools and the one big table which Tom Lincoln had made.

Within an hour the cabin was transformed. Abe's eyes grew round as he helped bring in the goods from the wagon. Plump featherbeds replaced the husk mattresses. They were spread with white sheets and gay calico quilts.

There was a shiny oak clothespress and two big rocking chairs padded with red carpet. A walnut bureau had big drawers and little ones. It even had a looking glass!

The Lincoln children had never seen such fine things. Abe could hardly believe that he was to have a featherbed to sleep on. The new boy, Johnny, helped him carry it to the loft.

"Johnny, your mammy must be awful rich," Abe said. "It's a wonder to me that she would marry a poor man like Pappy."

"She was awful lonesome after my pa died," Johnny said. "And she knowed your pappy from way back, when they was boy and girl together. No, she ain't rich. These are just the things we had at home. Look, Abe, Ma told me to give you something. She said it'd come better from me."

"Give me what?" Abe asked.

Johnny unrolled a bundle he had brought to the attic. "We're about the same size. Ma wants you to have my spare pants and a couple of shirts. And here's my other shoes, if you can wear them. I got two pairs."

Two pairs of shoes! In spite of what Johnny had said, his mother *must* be rich. Abe took the shoes that Johnny held out. They were not moccasins, but real leather shoes, made by a cobbler. Abe had never had real shoes before.

"Here's some socks," Johnny went on. He

[*41*]

looked down at Abe's bare feet. "Reckon you better wash, though. Before you get dressed up."

Abe flushed. Since Mammy and Aunt Betsy died, there had been no one to remind him about washing. Leaving Johnny in the loft, he hurried downstairs. The new mother was busy unpacking.

Abe's sister was unpacking dishes by the fireplace. Her brother hardly knew her. Sally's face was shining clean, her hair neatly combed. She was wearing a pretty pink dress, and shoes and stockings.

"Look what she give me, Abe," Sally whispered. "Sairey's bigger than I am, and her things are kind of a loose fit, but ain't they grand? Ma says as soon as she gets settled she'll make me some new dresses of my own. Oh, she's wonderful, Abe! I'm so glad Pappy brought her."

Abe was busy sloshing about with soapy water. He washed his face and hands, and then

[*42*]

his feet. Then he emptied the tin washpan and washed them all over again.

He climbed back to the loft. Johnny helped him put on the new clothes. The shoes were too small for his big feet. They pinched cruelly, but Abe did not feel the pain.

"Say, you look fine," Johnny said. "Go down and show Ma."

Abe went downstairs again. Shyly he stood before his new mother. "Johnny said to show you how I look," he mumbled.

Mrs. Lincoln was spreading a rag rug on the dirt floor. She jumped up and looked him over.

"A pretty good fit," she said, smiling. "Pants are too short for them long legs of yours, but they'll do till I can make you another pair. There's just one thing more. Sally, will you hand me that middle-sized butter crock?"

She took the yellow pottery bowl and put it on Abe's head like a hat. From somewhere she brought out a pair of scissors. Snip, snip,

Snip, snip, she went, around the rim of the bowl

she went, around the rim of the bowl. Abe's shaggy black hair fell in thick locks to the floor.

"There." Mrs. Lincoln took away the crock. With a friendly hand on Abe's shoulder she turned him to face the mirror. "Well, young fellow! How do you like yourself now?"

Abe stood and stared. It seemed to him he must be staring at some strange boy. The neatly trimmed hair, the clean cotton shirt, the carefully patched homespun trousers—surely this could not be Abe Lincoln? And Abe Lincoln with real shoes on his feet!

A slow smile broke over his solemn face. His eyes left the mirror. He looked all around the cabin. Crowded with the new things, it was cozy and homelike now. Last of all, he looked up into the kind face of his new mother.

"I think things are going to be all right," he told her. "I didn't know what to make of it at first. But reckon I'm right glad Pappy brought you, ma'am."

"Call me Ma," Sarah Lincoln said. "I ain't

[45]

trying to take your own mother's place, Abe. Nobody can do that. She'll always be your mammy. But now you got a mammy in heaven and a ma here on earth. It's natural you'd love her best. I hope you'll learn to love me a little bit, though."

"Won't be no trouble about that," Abe said shyly. "I—I reckon I've started already."

Mrs. Lincoln laughed. "That's good. I got some plans for you older children, Abe. Mr. Lincoln says the settlers have started a school up the creek. I'm a-going to send you young'-uns to it. You ever been to school, Abe?"

Abe's face brightened. "Me and Sally went a spell in Kentucky. I know my ABC's, and that's about all. I'd sure enough like to go again and learn more."

"Well, you will," Mrs. Lincoln said. "My Sairey now, she don't care nothing about school. All she can think of is prettying her-self up and making eyes at the boys. Reckon she'll marry the first one that asks her. She says book learning's no good to a girl nohow."

"Cousin Dennis says it's no good to a boy, neither," Abe said. "To hear him talk, all a man needs is good strong muscles. I don't see why you can't have muscles and book learning both. I'd like mighty well to have both."

"That's good sense," Mrs. Lincoln said. "Sairey and your big cousin can stay ignorant for all of me. But you and Johnny and Sally will start school as soon as your pappy can fix it. Will that suit you?"

"Yes, ma'am—Ma!" Abe's eyes were shining. "There ain't nothing you could have thought of that would suit me as good as going to school!"

CHAPTER FIVE

The Blab School

THE TEACHER had been prowling up
and down the room, making sure that everyone was at work. If he found any idlers, he
whacked their shoulders with his hickory stick.
Now he sat down at his desk, with his stick
near by. He took up the spelling book.

"Spelling, B class. Up front!" he said
sharply.

Two boys and three girls got up from their
benches. They came to stand in line before the
teacher's desk.

Abraham Lincoln peeped over the top of
his book. His sister Sally was in B class. He'd

[*48*]

like to know how she made out with the spelling. But the teacher was looking in his direction. Hastily he went back to his studying.

"C-i-r, cir; c-u-m, cum; v-e-n-t, vent; circumvent;" he read aloud.

All around him, the other pupils were shouting other words. This studying out loud was called "blabbing." Most of the country schools were "blab schools." The teachers thought it was the only way to make sure that the pupils were really studying.

The loud noise of blabbing did not disturb Abe's teacher. He roared out the spelling lesson to B class. The students yelled back their answers. Sally must have made out all right, Abe thought. She smiled at him as her class went back to their seats.

"Arithmetic, A class!" the teacher shouted. Only two boys came forward this time. This was the advanced class. It was the highest class in the one-room school. The teacher turned to the blackboard behind him. With a bit of chalk he wrote out a problem. Abe thought the two boys looked pretty scared. And no wonder. The problem was a difficult one.

Abe turned back to his lesson. Then the boy next to him gave him a poke. Sally had sent her slate along the row to him. Now he could write down the words as he spelled them.

Abe was proud of his penmanship. He wished he could practice more. He didn't get much chance at the slate which he shared with Johnny and Sally. After he had written the spelling lesson, he tried writing his own name in different ways. He wrote "A. Lincoln," big and bold, and "A. Lincoln" with fancy flourishes. He could not quite decide which way it looked best.

He was so busy that he hardly noticed what was happening up front. Both A class boys had failed to solve their problem. The teacher thrashed them soundly and sent them back to their seats. "Reading—C class!" he called next.

This was Abe's class. He went up front with

[50]

several other boys and girls. The teacher printed a sentence on the blackboard. With his stick he pointed at the biggest boy. "First word!" he barked.

The boy stared at the board. He shuffled his feet and looked helpless. Finally he shook his head.

"Dunce!" The teacher brought the stick down on the boy's shoulder. Then he pointed it at one of the girls. "First word," he repeated.

"Ann," the little girl read. The teacher nodded sourly and went on down the line. "Second word?" he asked the next boy.

So it went until he came to Abe. His was the fourth word, and the last in the sentence. Several students had missed it. Every one of them got a sharp blow from the stick. The teacher was frowning fiercely as he pointed at Abe. "Last word," he commanded.

"Flax," Abe said easily. " 'Ann can spin flax.' That's what it says, Teacher."

"I didn't ask you to read the whole sen-

"Look out you don't get too big for your

britches, young man!" the teacher said

tence," the teacher said angrily. "Look out you don't get too big for your britches, young man. I'll have no show-offs in my school. Now all together, class. Read!"

"Ann can spin flax!" the children shouted. They read the sentence over and over in chorus. Then they read it one by one. At last even the dullest boy read it perfectly. The teacher sent them back to their benches and rapped his desk with the stick. This meant that school was dismissed for the day.

The Lincoln children went home through the woods. Johnny ran ahead with some other boys, but Abe walked beside his sister Sally. He was frowning as he scuffed his way through the dry leaves.

"What's the matter, Abe?" his sister asked. "You ain't said a word."

"I'm mad," he answered. "I'm right good and mad. Wouldn't care if I never went back to that old school again."

"Why, Abe!" Sally stopped to stare at him.

*He was frowning as he scuffed his way
through the dry leaves*

"I thought you was crazy for school. You couldn't talk about nothing else when we first started. And you done so good, too. Teacher only kept you in the baby class the first day. Soon's he found out you knew all your letters, he moved you right up to C class. Don't see what you got to complain about."

"It's so slow. That's what I complain about," Abe answered. "First you got to know how to read and write all the letters. Then you got to go through the spelling book. They won't put you in reading class till you can spell great big words. And then what do you get to read? 'Ann can spin flax!' Who cares about Ann and her old flax? It's just plumb silly."

"Well, you have to get started," Sally urged. "That's how reading starts."

"All right, but I'm tired of starting," Abe said restlessly. "I can spell plenty of hard words. Bet I could read 'em, too, if I had me a book to read out of. Teacher won't even let me have a reader yet. I know I could read real good if I could just get hold of a book."

"We got a book at home," Sally pointed out. "The Bible. Did you ever try reading out of that?"

Abe glanced at her. The big leather-bound Bible was the family treasure. Births and deaths were recorded on the blank pages. The Bible was nothing for children to play with.

"I washed my hands good," Abe said abruptly. "I don't know what Ma would say if she caught me."

"Then you did try it!" Sally exclaimed. "You don't need to worry about Ma, Abe. She wouldn't care, long as you didn't dirty it. But the Bible's powerful hard reading."

"Not for me it ain't," Abe boasted. "Some of the names is jawbreakers, all right. But I made out pretty good, Sally. Course, I just sneaked a peek now and then when Ma was busy. I thought she'd tan my hide if she caught me."

"You don't know Ma very well yet," Sally answered. "She'd be right proud if one of us

[57]

young'uns could read out of the Bible. I'm a-going to ask her to let you read us a piece tonight."

Sally kept her promise. That night the family listened in amazement while young Abe read them the Twenty-third Psalm. He read it well, putting real expression into the beautiful words.

This was the beginning of Abe's reading. It began to seem that there would be no end to it. He would walk as much as twenty miles to borrow a book from a friendly neighbor. The trouble was there were so few books to borrow.

Once he got a book about the life of George Washington from a farmer named Josiah Crawford. Abe kept it in a crack of the cabin wall, near his bed in the loft. One night a heavy rain came through the crack and soaked the borrowed book.

Abe took it to the owner. "I'm right sorry about this, Mr. Crawford," he said. "I'll be glad to pay for the damage."

"Damage!" The old farmer looked angrily at the faded cover and wrinkled pages. "This book ain't damaged. It's plumb ruined. You'll give me the price of it, young man. Seventy-five cents I paid for it. If you got no money you'll work it out. I'll allow you twenty-five cents a day to cut cornstalks for me. Three days' work that'll be."

"All right, Mr. Crawford," Abe said. "I'll start tomorrow."

He worked for three days. Crawford let him keep the book. It was the first one the boy had ever owned.

Reading helped him through a new loneliness. In the old days, he and Cousin Dennis had always been together. Now Dennis had no time for anyone but pretty Sairey Johnston. Soon Dennis and Sairey were married. Abe and his father helped put up a new cabin for the young couple.

The first school had closed after one term. It was not until two years later that a new one

was opened. In all, Abe attended three schools
in Indiana. His stepbrother, Johnny Johnston,
soon had enough book learning to satisfy him.
Sally left the second school to marry a neighbor
boy. Abe went to school when his father could
spare him. But from books he was learning far

more than the backwoods schools could teach him. He sat up every night, reading while the others slept. To save his stepmother's candles, he read by firelight. He worked out arithmetic problems on the wooden fire shovel, with a burnt stick for his pencil.

So the years went by. Abe shot up to a great height; six feet four by his seventeenth birthday. He was very strong. Once he heard some men arguing about the best way to move a heavy log. While they talked, Abe picked up the log and put it where it belonged.

He worked on his father's farm, and he hired out to work for the neighbors. He cut down trees, hewed logs, and butchered hogs. He built a light flatboat and spent one summer running it as a ferry.

One day a farmer named Gentry spoke to him.

"I'd like to have you build a flatboat for me, Abe. Come spring, I aim to send a load of grain and hog meat down to New Orleans. Do you reckon you can do it?"

"You bet," Abe answered promptly. "Your boy Allen told me about it. He says he's going to take the load down."

"That's right. I ain't got the time to go myself. Say, Abe, would you like to go along? You're a handy boy with a boat. Allen will need another fellow with him."

"Go along? To New Orleans?" Abe drew a deep breath. "I'd sure enough like that, Mr. Gentry. I'll build you the best flatboat you ever see."

The farmer nodded. "Well, it's a bargain, Abe. Have her ready by the time spring gets here. I'm depending on you."

"She'll be ready," Abe promised.

CHAPTER SIX

Abe Sees Strange Sights

"SAY, that was good!" Abe said to Allen Gentry. "There ain't nothing like boating all day to make you relish your vittles at night."

He licked some bacon grease from his fingers and leaned back against a fallen log. Then he looked around the place where he and young Gentry were camping for the night, on the shore of the Ohio River. "Reckon we'll make Cairo tomorrow," he said.

"Reckon we will," Allen Gentry agreed. "That's where we hit the Mississippi, ain't it? And then we can go straight on down to New Orleans. What do you reckon a big city will look like, Abe? I ain't never seen one."

"Me neither," Abe admitted. "I've heard a heap about New Orleans, though. It was started by Frenchmen. They say lots of folks there still talk French. I aim to see all I can while we're there. I hope it takes a little while to trade our load."

"We'll *make* it take a while." Allen Gentry chuckled. "Pa didn't say nothing about hurrying back." He rose and stretched. "It's plumb dark now, Abe. We'd better turn in. We've got to get an early start tomorrow."

"You go ahead." Abe leaned forward to throw more wood on the fire. It blazed brightly, lighting up the little cove where the loaded flatboat was tied up to a stump.

Allen jumped aboard the flatboat. He pulled out a tangle of patchwork quilts. "Coming, Abe?" he called.

"Not yet. Pitch me that book that's under my coat, will you? I want to read a spell." Abe slumped comfortably back against the log. "That's it. *Statutes of the State of Indianny.*

[65]

A lawyer fellow loaned it to me, and he wants it back. Reckon I can work my way through it before we get home."

Allen held the book up to the firelight. He turned the pages quickly.

"Don't look very good reading to me," he said disgustedly. "Ain't even got no pictures in it. Statutes is sort of tombstones, ain't they? Ought to have some tombstone pictures."

"You're thinking about *statues*," Abe explained. "Statutes is something different. Statutes means laws."

"Well, why can't they say so? What do you want to read about laws for, anyhow?"

"I got a good reason." Abe smiled. "I had a little trouble with the law once, Allen. Got myself arrested. So I figure a fellow needs to know something about law to keep out of trouble."

"You got arrested? I never heard that." Allen forgot his sleepiness. He came back to sit beside the fire. "Tell me about it," he coaxed.

[*66*]

" 'Taint much of a story," Abe began. "Happened when I was ferrying down at Bates's Landing last summer. You know the Dill brothers? They live over on the Kentucky side."

Allen nodded. "They run the big ferry across the Ohio, don't they? Pretty tough boys, from all I hear."

"They think they're tough." Abe grinned. "Well, I wasn't hurting their business none with my little ferry. But they claimed I was. One day John Dill called me over to the Kentucky side. Soon's I got ashore, him and his brother Lin jumped on me.

"They was a-going to throw me in the river, but I showed them they couldn't do that. I grabbed one in each hand and knocked their heads together, easy as pie. Well, then they said they'd have me arrested for ferrying without a license. I dared them to do it."

Abe paused. "Go on!" Allen said breathlessly. "Did you get put in jail?"

"Let me tell it, can't you? We went off to see the judge. Old Squire Pate it was; a mighty fine man. Squire held the trial right there on his front porch. John Dill spoke first and said he wanted to get me arrested. Then it was my turn.

"I stood up and told how I ferried passengers out to the steamers. You know there ain't no good dock for big boats at Bates's Landing. The steamers have to stop out in midstream. All I done was take folks out to board them. When I told Squire this, he looked in the Statutes and read us the law about ferries."

"You mean the law that said you had to have a license?" Allen asked.

"That's it," Abe replied. "The law says you got to have a license to ferry passengers *across* the river. It don't say a word about ferrying folks out to the middle, like I done. So I didn't break no law. Squire said so. He told the Dills to get out and quit wasting his time."

"Say, that was lucky," Allen said. "Wasn't you scared?"

"Not a bit," Abe answered. "You couldn't be, not with Squire Pate. He let me stay and talk to him after the Dills left. He said citizens ought to know more about their laws. So I'm trying to find out. The trouble is, there are so many different kinds. All the states have got their own laws. What's against the law in one state is all right in another. It's mighty confusing."

Allen yawned. "I don't need to know no laws. If I break one the sheriff'll be around to tell me. I'm going to bed, Abe. You set up and crack your brain over laws if you're a mind to."

Leaving Abe to his book, Allen went to bed. The next day the boys reached Cairo and and started down the Mississippi River.

The trip down the broad Mississippi took several days. It was easy enough, for the current carried the flatboat along. The boys had only to guide it around bends and sandbars. For this they used long poles, plunging them down to the river's muddy bed. Every night they tied up and cooked supper on the bank.

[69]

They reached New Orleans safely on a busy Saturday morning. They had a good offer for their load even before they left the dock.

"We'll think it over," Allen said importantly. "We'll let you know in a day or so, mister." He winked at Abe. Now they would not have to hunt for a buyer. And the boys were free to explore the city.

They walked open-mouthed through the streets, gaping at the houses built of brick and stone. These looked strange to eyes that knew only log cabins. They peeped in at stores displaying fine French furniture, silver, and jewelry. They watched the glittering carriages dash by, carrying richly dressed ladies and gentlemen.

They passed the Opera House and came to the magnificent Cathedral. The doors were open. Abe and Allen hung about, wishing they had courage to venture inside. "Folks say it's a church," Allen whispered. "But shucks, nobody builds a meeting house that grand!"

"I never knew they built them this big," Abe said. "I reckon we better not go in, Allen. We wouldn't know how to act. Let's get out of this neighborhood. It's too tony for me. There must be some place where our kind of folks live."

The boys chose another street and followed where it led. The handsome stores gave way to warehouses. Soon they came out in a small square. In the center was a platform, surrounded by a crowd of people.

"What's going on?" Allen asked a man near him.

"It is an auction, young sir," the man answered politely. "A shipload has just arrived from Virginia." He spoke English with a French accent. The boys could scarcely understand him.

"What did he say?" Abe asked as they moved up.

"They're auctioning off something, from what I could make out," Allen answered.

[71]

"Push on up front, Abe. Might as well see what there is to see."

It did not take them long to find out what the Frenchman had meant. This was a slave auction. Negro slaves were here to be sold, as cattle are sold, in the open market.

Now the white auctioneer took his place on the platform. One of the Negroes was shoved up beside him.

"Good strong field hand!" the auctioneer shouted. "Step up, gentlemen. Feel his muscles. What am I offered for this fine healthy boy? What's that, sir? No, he ain't lazy. You, Rastus, jump around. Run a little. Show the gentleman how fast you can move. You see, sir? Quick and willing. And strong as an ox. Now. What am I bid?"

Abe pulled at Allen's sleeve. "Come on. I've had enough of this." He hurried his companion out of the crowd and around the corner.

The younger boy looked at him curiously.

"What's the hurry, Abe? I thought that was right interesting. I ain't never seen nothing like it before."

"Me neither. And I hope I never do again!" Abe's voice was shaking. "Oh, I've seen slaves back in Kentucky. They was just hard-worked colored folks, far's I could tell. I knew they was bought and sold. But it's different when

[73]

you see it done. Makes me sick to my stomach, and that's the truth. Let's get back to the boat."

He pulled his friend along with him. It was nearly dark now. Lights came on in the shops and houses. Orchestras were tuning up in the dance halls. A burst of song drifted from the open door of a saloon. New Orleans was at its gayest when night came.

Allen Gentry would have liked to linger. But Abe strode on without looking to left or right. The slave auction had spoiled all his pleasure in city sights.

A few days later the boys started home. When he got back to Indiana, Abe found that his father had work for him to do. Mr. Lincoln had decided to build a new and larger cabin.

Abe set to work helping to cut and trim the logs. But the new home was never finished. Winter brought a return of the dreaded milk-sick. Tom Lincoln began to talk about finding a better place to live than Little Pigeon Creek.

A Kentucky cousin, John Hanks, had settled in Illinois. Cousin John wrote that the milksick was unknown there. And besides, his letter went on, Illinois land was better for farming. He urged the Lincolns to come and settle near him.

Mr. Lincoln liked the idea of moving to Illinois. Dennis Hanks offered to visit Cousin John and see for himself what it was like.

When Dennis came home, Mr. Lincoln called all the family together. Sairey brought her four small children with her. And Tildy, who had married a young man named Levi Hall, arrived with her baby in her arms.

"Everybody keep quiet now," Mr. Lincoln ordered, when everyone was seated. "I want you all to hear what Dennis has to tell us."

CHAPTER SEVEN

Abe Lincoln Uses His Head

W<small>ELL</small>, that's how it is." Cousin Dennis looked around the circle of faces. "I tell you Cousin John Hanks wasn't lying about his farm.

"There's mighty fine country in Illinois. Real prairie, with no trees to chop down before you can lay out a field. And the soil's the richest I ever did see. I think we'd be fools if we didn't go."

"It sounds good," Tom Lincoln agreed. "I'm getting mighty discouraged with Indianny. My corn crop's been poor this year. And now the milksick's going round again. I'd just as soon light out. What do you say, Sarah?"

"I'm agreeable," said Mrs. Lincoln, who sat by the fire, with Tildy's baby in her arms. "If you menfolks are set on it, us women'll follow along. That's right, ain't it, girls?" She smiled at her two daughters.

"It suits us," Sairey Hanks declared. "Me and Tildy are thinking about the children. Looks like they'll have a better chance in Illinois. And we're right scared of the milksick. Some of the young'uns up the creek has got it real bad. I don't care how soon we get out of here."

"Well, Abe? Johnny?" Dennis said eagerly. "You two are the bachelors among us. You got no young'uns to worry about. But setting aside the milksick, there *are* better chances in Illinois. For children and for grown folks too. I been there, and I know. What do you say?"

"I don't see nothing against it," Abe said slowly.

Johnny Johnston gave a whoop of delight.

[77]

"Then that settles it!" he declared. "I been for it all the time. Now we're all agreed. Abe, me and you and Pappy will start building a wagon tomorrow. It'll have to be a monstrous big one, to haul us all to Illinois."

All was ready when spring came. The huge covered wagon was loaded with household goods of the three families. The grownups in the party were Mr. and Mrs. Lincoln, their two daughters and their husbands, Abe and his stepbrother Johnny. The four Hanks children and Baby John Hall brought the number up to thirteen.

They left Pigeon Creek on a cold March day. Before leaving, however, Mrs. Lincoln and Abe took armfuls of evergreen boughs to the little family burying ground in the woods.

Aunt Betsy and Uncle Thomas Sparrow lay there, and Abe's young mother. Near them was a newer grave. Abe's sister Sally had died just before he made the New Orleans trip. Sadly he helped his stepmother cover the lonely graves with green branches. Then he knelt beside her while she said a farewell prayer.

Two weeks later Tom Lincoln stopped his wagon before John Hanks's door. John Hanks had already been in Illinois for several years. Now he helped his relatives to get settled and build their cabins.

Abe's job was to split rails for a fence around his father's new farm. Because of his great

[79]

strength and skill he could split more rails in a day than any man in the neighborhood. Soon he and his axe were in great demand among the other farmers.

One day he was splitting rails for a neighbor when a strange man rode up and stopped his horse.

"Are you Abraham Lincoln?" the stranger asked. "John Hanks said I'd find you here."

Abe looked up. The newcomer was a fat man, well dressed in frock coat and stovepipe hat. He was riding a good horse with an expensive saddle. Abe had never seen him before.

"Denton Offut is my name," the man went on. "It's a pretty well known name around Lexington, Kentucky, where I come from. I'm out here in Illinois to do business. Hanks recommended you for a little deal I have in mind. What do you say we sit down in the shade and talk it over?"

Abe shook his head. "Sorry, mister. I can't spare the time now. Major Warnick is a-paying me forty cents a day to split these rails. It'd be cheating him if I knocked off work just to talk for a spell."

Mr. Offut nodded approvingly. " 'Honest Abe'—Hanks says that's what they call you around here. I can see why. Well, an honest man is just what I'm looking for. You quit at sundown, I reckon? Come over to your cousin John Hanks's house then. I'll talk to you there."

When his work was done, Abe walked over to his cousin's home. Mr. Offut was there. He explained that he meant to take a big boatload of corn and pork down to New Orleans. He would need a crew of three. John Hanks had already been hired.

"Three men for one boat!" Abe exclaimed in surprise. "You don't need that many, mister. Me and Allen Gentry made out all right, just the two of us."

"Yes, but your trip with Gentry was small potatoes beside this," John Hanks put in. "Mr. Offut's talking about a flatboat eighty feet long. She'll carry live hogs as well as the other stuff."

"Oh, I see," Abe answered. "Well, I don't mind if I join you, Mr. Offut. You say you want another fellow too? How about my step-brother, Johnny Johnston? He's right handy on the water."

Mr. Offut agreed, and Johnny was hired. Abe, Johnny, and John Hanks built the giant flatboat. They worked in the woods near

[*82*]

Springfield, Illinois, on the Sangamon River.

Building the flatboat took nearly six weeks. At last the boat was ready. Mr. Offut came with several wagonloads of goods. They were put aboard, and the trip began.

The boat, with Mr. Offut as passenger, moved off down the Sangamon. All went well until they rounded a bend in the river at the little Illinois village of New Salem.

"That's a mill dam up ahead," John Hanks said anxiously. "Hope the boat will go over it all right. I don't know what we'll do if we get stuck there."

Even while he spoke, the flatboat reached the dam. The front part sailed smoothly over. But the middle struck the dam and stayed fast.

John Hanks and Abe and Johnny tried everything they could think of to free the boat. But it would not move.

People came out from the village to help. They offered to remove the load in their boats. This was done, but the flatboat did not budge.

Hours went by. The New Salem men helped
the crew push and pull. They tried one scheme
after another. Nothing seemed to help. Mr.
Offut was getting very worried.

Then Abe Lincoln had an idea. "We could bore a hole in the bottom of the front end," he said. "The back end is full of water now. If we lifted the back end and let the water run to the front—seems like that ought to tilt her over. What do you think, Mr. Offut?"

"How do I know?" Offut snapped. "I'm not a river man. But you've got to get the boat over some way. If you think your scheme will work, go ahead and try it."

Lincoln bored a hole in the bottom of the end of the boat that stuck out over the dam. Then all the men worked together to lift the rear end. The water ran to the front and out of the hole Abe had made.

Yes, the scheme was working! As they watched, the front end dipped down under the weight of the water. The back rose higher in the air. Slowly the big boat slid over the dam and dropped into the river on the other side.

A cheer went up from the crowd. Mr. Offut grasped Abe's hand. "That was using your head, my boy," he shouted. "I won't forget this!"

The hole was plugged up and the boat was loaded again. The men continued their voyage. Abe's success with the boat had made a deep impression on Mr. Offut. "I can use a bright young man like you in my business," he told him.

All the way to New Orleans, Mr. Offut talked about business. He had liked New Salem, where the boat had been stuck. It was a new settlement, and growing fast. Mr. Offut thought a store would do well there. Also, someone had told him that the mill was for sale or rent.

"How'd you like to run the store for me?" he asked Abe.

"I don't know," Abe answered slowly. "I never done that kind of work. Don't know if I could."

"Of course you could," Mr. Offut answered. "You're honest, and you're smart. Look how you got the boat over the dam when they said it couldn't be done. And you did it just by using your head! You come in with me, and you won't be sorry."

"Reckon maybe you're right," Abe said. "I'll try it, anyway."

The trip to New Orleans was a successful one. As soon as they returned, Mr. Offut began his preparations for opening his store at New Salem. Abe went home to tell his family of the new plans. Then he left his log cabin home for good. His life as farmer and rail splitter was over.

CHAPTER EIGHT

Adventures in New Salem

ABE left his carpetbag at the tavern and and strolled out for his first good look at New Salem.

The two or three stores looked clean and neat. He counted fifteen cabins strung out along the river. Upstream he could see the mill and the dam where the boat had hung. Everything here was new, for the town had only been settled a short time.

Across the road a knot of men were gathered in front of one of the houses. An American flag flew from the window. Just outside the open door a man sat at a rough board table.

"Hey, bub!" Abe hailed a barefoot boy. "What's going on over there?"

The boy grinned. "Election Day, mister. Teacher's a-taking the vote. No school for us!"

The youngster turned a happy handspring in the dusty street. Abe laughed and crossed over to the voting place.

For a little while he stood quietly watching. He knew about elections. He had never seen one. A few years before, Pappy and Cousin Dennis had walked eight miles to vote for General Andy Jackson. Abe had not been old enough to vote then. He had not paid much attention. So this was how it was done!

The voting was very simple. There was no secret ballot. Each man stepped up to the schoolteacher and gave his name. The teacher wrote the name in a big book. Then the voter spoke his choices for Congressman, justice of the peace, and constable. These were written down after his name.

Presently the teacher laid down his quill

pen. He took out a red cotton handkerchief and wiped his perspiring face.

"You'll have to give me a rest, boys," he said to the voters. "I've been at this since sunup, and my hand's getting cramped. I was supposed to have a helper, but he hasn't shown up. It's too much for one man."

"I'd be glad to give you a hand," a farmer said. "But I got to get right back to my cornfield. I reckon we're all in the same fix. We just can't spare the whole day, Mr. Graham."

Mentor Graham thanked him politely and smiled. He knew that the man who had spoken could barely write his own name. This was true of most of the other voters.

Mr. Graham sat back in his chair, rubbing his aching wrist. Then his eyes fell on the tall stranger leaning quietly against the fence. He at least seemed to have plenty of time.

"You, young sir," the teacher called. "Can you write?"

Abe came up to the table. "Reckon I can

make a few chicken tracks," he said modestly.

"Show me." The teacher handed him the pen. In careful, plain letters Abe wrote his name, "A. Lincoln."

Graham looked at the scrap of paper. "Might as well write it over again in the book," he said. "You're past twenty-one, aren't you? And a citizen of Illinois? All right. Then go ahead and put down your vote."

"I'd rather wait a little," Abe said slowly. "I'm a stranger here. I don't know who's a-running, nor who's the best man. Would it be all right if I didn't vote till later in the day?"

"Certainly," the teacher answered. "But if you're going to be around, I'd be much obliged if you'd give me a hand. I'll give you a full day's pay."

It was easy work for Abe. He and Mentor Graham took turns writing in the big book. The voters were pleasant and friendly. They were anxious to persuade Abe to vote for their favorites. But he asked some very shrewd questions before he finally cast his first vote.

The men were in no great hurry to leave after they had voted. They lounged in the shade, laughing and talking. When it was Abe's turn to rest he joked with them, telling them funny stories.

He had been a little shy of town people at first. His shyness soon wore off. He joined in a wrestling match and threw three men in turn.

It seemed that all these strangers liked him. By the time the voting ended, they were no longer strangers. He had begun to feel at home in New Salem.

When the last vote was counted, Mentor Graham asked, "Where are you staying, Abe?"

"Say, I never give it no thought," Abe answered. "I meant to find me some place to board. My bag's at Rutledge's Tavern. But I can't stay there. It costs too much."

"You might get in at Reverend Cameron's," Graham suggested. "They take a boarder now

[*93*]

By the time the voting ended,

they were no longer strangers

and then. Mrs. Cameron is mighty strict, though. She won't have a drinking man in her house."

"That's all right. I don't drink, nor gamble neither," Abe answered. "A preacher's house will suit me fine. Maybe they got some books to read."

"I'll walk over with you," Graham said. "Like to read, do you? Well, now, maybe you'd be interested in our debating society. We get together every Friday night to discuss politics and history, and literature. I'll take you next Friday if you care to go. Here's the Cameron place."

Abe settled comfortably into the household. A few nights later he went with Mr. Graham to the debating society. Abe sat listening in silence through the first meeting. At the second one, he got to his feet and made a short speech.

"Hope you didn't think I was too forward," he said anxiously to Mentor Graham on the way home. "Something the lawyer said put me in mind of something else. I was on my feet before I knew it. Was it all right for me to talk?"

"We were glad to hear you, Abe," Mr. Graham said. "Your speech was sensible, and you put your thought clearly. The funny story at the end made them laugh, but it proved your point too. That's fine. But there's just one thing, Abe. Your grammar is bad. If you're going to speak in public, you ought to correct it."

"I been thinking about that," Abe admitted. "I know I don't talk good grammar. I never paid no attention. Everybody out my way talks like I do. But hearing you and them lawyers at the debating society—oh, I take notice how different I sound. Do you reckon I'm too old to learn any better?"

"Certainly not," Graham said briskly. "All you need is a good book on grammar. If you study it the way you study other books, you'll soon speak as correctly as anyone."

Abe's first month at New Salem was a busy one. He helped Mr. Offut build his store and make the counters and shelves. At night, tired as he was, he sat up late with a borrowed grammar book. Mentor Graham congratulated him on the way his speech improved.

When the new store opened, Abe had full charge of it. Denton Offut had rented the mill, and was running it himself. Mr. Offut boasted around town about his smart young clerk. "Abe's a boy who knows how to use his head," he told his friends. "And not only that. He's the strongest fellow around here. He can run faster and wrestle better than any man in the county."

He made this boast many times. One day a man said to him, "You talk mighty big, Mr. Offut. But we raise some good wrestlers around here, too. I'd like to see this boy of yours stand up against Jack Armstrong. I bet Jack would have him on the ground in two minutes."

"We'll see about that," Offut answered

promptly. "Bring on this Armstrong. We'll fix up a match between him and Abe."

"Shucks, mister, you don't want to do that," another man put in. "Jack Armstrong's the leader of the Clary's Grove boys. They're the toughest gang you ever saw. And Jack's the toughest of the lot. He'll make mincemeat of your clerk."

"We'll see," Offut repeated. "Now look here. There's a vacant lot next to my store. We'll have a wrestling match between the two boys. That'll settle who's the best wrestler. You fellows tell Armstrong. I'll fix it up with Abe."

The contest was held a few days later. A big crowd gathered. Young Armstrong brought his gang of rough young fellows who lived on the edge of town. Armstrong was smiling as he stripped off his coat. He could not remember the last time he had lost a wrestling match. He was sure he would win this one.

A few minutes later he was not so sure. Abe

[*99*]

The two swayed back and forth,

while the crowd shouted

was a master of all the holds. His powerful arms were like bands of iron. The two swayed back and forth, while the crowd shouted. Then, losing his temper, Armstrong brought his heavy boot down on Lincoln's foot. A cry of "Foul, foul!" went up from Abe's friends.

Armstrong had broken the rules for fair wrestling. Abe was so angry that he seized his opponent by the throat and lifted him high in the air. He shook him violently and then threw him to the ground.

This was too much for the Clary's Grove gang. They rushed toward Abe with raised fists. But Jack Armstrong was picking himself up. He came over to Abe and held out his hand.

"I deserved what I got," he said with a grin. "You're a better man than I am, Abe Lincoln. Here's my hand on it."

From that time on, Abe and the Clary's Grove boys were the best of friends. But these boys could never understand Abe. They could not see why a champion wrestler would want to waste his time making speeches.

Abe's friends in the debating society could not see why he wanted to waste time with the Clary's Grove boys. Abe himself tried to explain his feeling. "I don't just like one kind of people," he said. "I like all kinds of people. Reckon I just like *people*."

Abe liked people, and people liked him. His speeches at the debating society were attracting attention. One night after a meeting one of the members spoke to him.

"Abe," he said, "what would you think about running for the State Legislature? We think you'd be a good man to represent us in the Statehouse up at Vandalia."

"Me?" Abe stared at him. "Shucks, you wouldn't want me on a job like that. The men in the Legislature make laws for all the people in Illinois. A fellow would have to know a lot to help make laws. I read lawbooks whenever I can get hold of them. I'm beginning to learn a little about the law. But I don't know enough yet to try my hand at *making* laws."

"We think you know plenty," his friend said. "Think it over, Abe. We'll talk about it again before election time comes round."

Abe did think about it. The more he thought, the more he liked the idea. But he knew he would have to make some good speeches to get elected. He began preparing his speeches.

One day he was working over a speech in the store. He had plenty of spare time now. The store was not doing very well. Mr. Offut was careless about ordering new goods when the old ones were sold. The truth was that Denton Offut had lost interest in New Salem. He was already talking about moving to some bigger place, where business was better.

Abe was hard at work on his speech when the door opened. He looked up, and then laid down his pen with a smile.

"Jack Armstrong!" he said. "What brings you to town so early?"

"Ain't you heard, Abe?" Jack asked. "Old Chief Black Hawk is on the warpath. He claims this is all Injun land and us white settlers have got to get out."

Abe smiled. "In a way, you can't blame the old chief for being mad," he said. "We white folks came in here and took away the Indians' hunting land. Oh, we bought it and paid for it. But it seems like Indians just don't understand what they did when they sold their land. So Black Hawk is going to put us out, is he?"

"It ain't funny, Abe," Armstrong insisted. "He's got a big crowd of warriors with him. The Governor has called for volunteers. Me and all the Clary's Grove boys are a-going to enlist. How about you, Abe?"

Abe looked around the store. He had not had a customer all morning. Many of the shelves were empty. Soon the store would have to close up. Then he would be out of a job.

"Well, Jack," he said slowly, "I'm a right good shot with a squirrel gun. Maybe I'd not make such a bad soldier. I'll enlist with you."

[105]

CHAPTER NINE
A Man with Three Jobs

ABE LINCOLN spent three months as a soldier in the Black Hawk War. He never got near the fighting. Chief Black Hawk kept to the northern part of Illinois. He was finally captured when he crossed into what is now Wisconsin.

Abe's group, which was guarding central and southern Illinois, never had to fire a shot. But in the long marches and the hardships of camp life, Lincoln did learn something of what a soldier has to endure.

He came back to New Salem ten days before Election Day. He did not have much hope of being elected to the State Legislature. There was no time to make all the speeches he had planned. He made as many as he could. But when the election came, he was defeated.

While Abe was at war, Mr. Offut had closed the store, given up the mill, and left town. Abe now joined a friend named Bill Berry in buying a store that was for sale.

One day Mentor Graham, the schoolmaster, dropped in at the store. He found Abe lying full length on the counter, reading a book.

"Is this how you do business?" Mr. Graham asked with a laugh.

Lincoln looked up. Then he swung his long legs over the counter.

"Morning, Mr. Graham," he said. "Yes, I reckon this is a fair sample of business around here. Fact is, there just isn't any. If things don't pick up pretty soon, we'll be going bust."

"You never should have let Berry talk you into this, Abe," Graham said seriously.

"You're not cut out for storekeeping. What's that you're reading?"

"*Blackstone's Commentaries,*" Abe replied, holding up the book. "The store did bring me one piece of good luck, Mr. Graham. A fellow stopped by the other day with a barrel of stuff he wanted to trade. He needed food for his family, and I traded for the barrel just to help him out.

"The barrel was mostly filled with trash. But right down at the bottom I found a whole set of Blackstone. It's something I've always wanted to own."

"Blackstone, eh?" the schoolmaster said. "Those are the first books you have to study if you want to be a lawyer. Are you planning to take up the law, Abe? You'd be good at it. Better than at storekeeping."

"I think so too," Abe agreed. "If I can ever learn enough."

"From what I've seen of you, you can learn anything you want to learn," Mr. Graham said. "Listen, Abe. Some of the important men around town are talking about you. They still think you ought to represent us in the Legislature. There'll be another election in two years. We'll want you to run again."

"Well, shucks, Mr. Graham, that's mighty good to hear," Abe said. "I'd like to take another crack at it. The only trouble is—well, I don't see how I can stay in New Salem till election. We'll have to close this store pretty soon.

"I'll be out of a job then, and likely loaded down with debts too. There'll be nothing to do but go back to my father's farm. I can always make a living splitting rails, I reckon."

Mr. Graham smiled. "We can't lose you, Abe. We'll find work for you here in town. Now let me see. Old Man Hill, the postmaster, is in pretty poor health. He's talking about giving up the post office. We'll get him to recommend you for postmaster.

"You can help out in his store, too. And

there's something else. The county surveyor wants an assistant. Do you know anything about surveying?"

"I don't know surveying, but I can borrow a book and learn," Abe said. "Mr. Graham, that's three jobs you've thought up for me! Postmaster, clerk for Mr. Hill, and surveyor. That ought to keep me going for a while."

"The three jobs will keep you going for two years," his friend answered. "Then election comes round again. And this time you'll have a real job. You'll represent this county in the State Legislature."

Mr. Graham's plan worked out exactly as he had predicted. The Lincoln-Berry store failed, but Abe made a fair living from the three jobs. When election came he won over his opponent. He went to Vandalia, the state capital, to help make the laws for Illinois.

The next few years were happy ones for Abe Lincoln. When the Legislature was not meeting, he spent his time in New Salem. He lived at the tavern kept by Mr. Rutledge. The tavern keeper had a pretty daughter named Ann. One summer Lincoln asked Ann to be his wife. He was the happiest man in the world when she said "Yes."

But the happiness soon changed to sorrow. Before they could plan their wedding, Ann fell ill of a fever. She died a week later.

[*111*]

Abe was heartbroken. In his lonely grief, he turned away from his friends. Fiercely he threw himself into the study of law. In the year after Ann's death, he was admitted to practice law in the State of Illinois.

CHAPTER TEN

Happy Days

ONE sunny morning Abraham Lincoln tied his horse outside a store at Springfield, Illinois. He carried his leather saddlebags inside with him. The store owner, Joshua Speed, looked up.

"Morning, Mr. Lincoln," he said. "Welcome to Springfield. But you're a little early. The Legislature won't meet for several weeks."

"I know that," Lincoln answered. "It'll be the first meeting since the capital was moved to Springfield. You people worked hard to get your town made the capital, instead of Vandalia."

[*113*]

"Yes, we did work hard to get the law passed," Speed said. "And you were a big help, Mr. Lincoln. I heard your speech in favor of moving the capital. That speech made you a lot of friends here in Springfield."

"I'm glad to hear it," Lincoln answered. "Because I'm going to be one of you now. I'm going into the law business with a fellow I met in the army. You know Lawyer John Stuart?"

"I certainly do," Speed said. "He's a friend of mine. So you're going to settle in Springfield, Mr. Lincoln. Where are you staying?"

"That's what I wanted to talk to you about," Lincoln said. "I aim to sleep in the office. I know where I can get a bedstead. What'll you charge me for mattress, pillows, and covers? It's a small single bed."

"Let's see." Speed took a slate and figured it out. "That'll be seventeen dollars."

Lincoln's smile faded. "Seventeen? Too steep for me. Oh, I reckon it's cheap enough. The truth is, I've only got seven dollars. Could you trust me till Christmas? If I do all right in the law business, I can pay you then. If I don't —well, I don't know if I can ever pay you."

Mr. Speed smiled. He liked this honest young man who was not ashamed to admit that he was poor.

"Mr. Lincoln," he said, "I have a better plan. I'm a bachelor. I've fixed myself up a big room over the store. Why don't you move in with me? I'd be proud to have you."

Abe grinned. "Where is your room?" he asked.

Speed pointed to the stairway. Abe picked up his saddlebags. They held all he owned, a little clothing and his law books. He clattered up the stairs.

A minute later he was back without the bags.

"Speed," he said cheerfully, "I've moved in."

The law business went very well. Abe "rode the circuit," traveling from town to town where the courts were in session. He met all the important men in his part of the state. His fine mind and gentle, kindly manner won friends wherever he went.

Lincoln's best friends were in Springfield, where he lived. The ladies there often invited him to their parties. He hated to go, for he felt awkward and clumsy in society. He could never learn to dance well. He said his feet were too big. He was always afraid he would step on a partner's toes and crush them.

Joshua Speed, Lincoln's roommate, liked parties. One night he insisted that Abe go with him to the home of Mrs. Ninian Edwards. Mrs. Edwards was giving a dance for her sister, who had come on a visit from Kentucky.

Lincoln let himself be persuaded for once. That night he met Mrs. Edwards' sister, beautiful Mary Todd. Three years later, Miss Todd became his wife.

The young couple went to live at a Springfield hotel. Then, when their son, Robert, was

That night he met the beautiful Mary Todd

born, Lincoln bought a house. It was a two-story wooden building, painted white, set in a wide yard. The Lincolns lived there as long as they remained in Springfield. Robert's little brothers were born there.

The busy, happy years went by. Lincoln was becoming better known all the time. He served one term in the Congress at Washington. When the term ended, he was glad to move his family back to Springfield. There, with his boys growing up in the simple home, surrounded by friendly neighbors, Lincoln passed the happiest days of his life.

CHAPTER ELEVEN

Lincoln Loses—and Wins

Papa's coming, Mama." Eight-year-old Willie Lincoln turned from the window. "He's stopped to talk to that old colored lady that sells greens. Can Tad and I go to meet him, Mama?"

"*May* we," his mother corrected. "Yes, you boys run along. And tell your father to hurry. His supper is drying up in the oven."

The two little boys scampered off. Mrs. Lincoln turned to her oldest son.

"I declare, I don't know what to make of your father," she said with a helpless laugh. "He hasn't had a meal at home for two days.

[*119*]

He spends all his time at the Republican convention. I suppose it's over, or we wouldn't be seeing him now. But instead of coming home, he dawdles along talking to that old peddler."

"Well, that's Papa for you." Robert Lincoln smiled.

He was a handsome boy, not quite fifteen. Like his younger brothers, Robert looked more like his pretty mother than his homely father. Abraham Lincoln was proud of his good-looking family.

"I wish he'd come, so we can get it over with," Robert went on a little nervously. "I dread asking him. After all, it'll cost a lot of money."

"Now, Bob, we've settled that," Mrs. Lincoln said. "Your father is doing well in his law business. He can afford to send his son East to a good school. We'll—"

Her words were drowned in a burst of noise. The door opened and then slammed shut. Tad's puppy was jumping around Mr. Lincoln, barking furiously. The little boys were both talking at once. They clung to their father, who carried a big market basket.

"Here, here, let me get my breath."

Abraham Lincoln shook off the little boys and handed his tall hat to Willie. Still carrying the basket, he came to kiss his wife.

"Mary, my dear, I know I'm very late. But I've brought you a present to excuse my tardiness."

He held out the basket. Mary poked in it with her white fingers. "I don't see anything but some old wilted leaves," she said.

"Those are dandelion greens, my dear," her husband explained. "Boil them with a good chunk of salt pork, and there's nothing better. Aunt Sukey picked them this morning with the dew on them. She carried them five miles to town. But it seems nobody wanted to buy greens today. I couldn't let the poor old soul trudge home again with them, could I? So I told her you'd be glad to have them."

"I never cared much for greens," Mary Lincoln said. "Well, take the basket to the kitchen, boys. And tell Maria that Mr. Lincoln is ready for his supper now. I don't suppose it'll be fit to eat by this time," she added.

"I've had supper," Lincoln said. "Ate at the tavern with some of the fellows. All I want now is a little peace and quiet."

He slipped out of his long coat and threw it on the couch. Then, with a sigh of relief, he sank into his favorite rocking chair.

Mrs. Lincoln picked up the coat and hung it in the closet. She had given up trying to cure her husband of his untidy ways.

"Here are your slippers, Papa."

The younger boys had come back from the kitchen. Willie pulled off his father's heavy boots while five-year-old Tad brought the green carpet slippers.

"Well, that's better," Lincoln said gratefully.

He leaned back, rocking gently, and looked

around at the pleasant family scene. His wife had returned to the sofa and taken up her crochet work. Robert was at the desk in the corner, pretending to read.

"What have you got there, Bob?" Lincoln called. "Is it a new book?"

"It's not a book. It's something that came in the mail today."

Young Robert caught his mother's encouraging glance. He got up and came to his father's chair, holding out the small booklet.

Lincoln took it and read the title. *"Exeter Academy, Exeter, New Hampshire.* Well, let's see." Rapidly he turned the pages. "Algebra, rhetoric, ancient and modern history—say, they teach everything, don't they? And Latin and Greek, by jingo! You want to learn all that, Bob?"

"Yes, sir." Bob gulped. "I'd like to go to Exeter, Papa. And after that I'd like to go to Harvard College. I know it'll cost a lot. But I think an education is worth all it costs."

"Well, so do I, son," Abe Lincoln said. "So do I. I want to give my boys the education I never had. This Exeter Academy looks like the very place for you, Bob."

"You mean I can go? I really can? Oh, Papa!"

Bob's handsome face glowed, as his father nodded.

Presently Abe Lincoln turned to his wife.

"Got a speck of news myself," he said mildly. "This scheme of Bob's drove it out of my head. The convention nominated me to-day, Mary. I'm going to run for United States Senator."

"You are?" Mrs. Lincoln asked in surprise. "Will you run against Stephen Douglas? I know he's up for re-election."

"Yes," her husband answered. "The Republicans think I can beat our friend Douglas. It won't be easy, though. We thought we'd challenge him to some joint debates. He and I would speak from the same platform. Each of us telling why he should be elected. That ought to bring the voters out."

"What'll you tell them, Papa?" Robert asked. "You always said Judge Douglas is a good man."

"Steve Douglas is a good man and my good friend," Lincoln answered quickly. "But just the same, he's not the man to be in the Senate right now. The way he feels about slavery makes him dangerous."

"I don't see that," Mrs. Lincoln put in. "Mr. Douglas is in favor of slavery. Well, so are lots of nice people. My father owned slaves back in Kentucky. He always treated them kindly."

"I am sure he did, my dear." Lincoln sighed. "But any way you look at it, slavery is wrong. A human being has a right to be free."

Little Willie looked up at his father.

"Will you set the slaves free when you're elected, Papa?"

"I wish I could, my boy." Lincoln's eyes

were sad. "But you see, our states make their own laws. Some states have laws saying slavery is all right. We can't do anything about that. But new states will be coming into the Union. We can see that they come in with laws against slavery."

"Who's *we?*" Willie asked.

"The United States Congress," his father answered. "That's why I want to go to the Senate. That's why I don't want Douglas there. He'd help the new states to be slave-owning states. I'd try to see that they were free states."

Willie looked puzzled. "But I thought the states made their own laws," he said. "Can the Congress make bigger laws, then?"

"Yes, it can," Lincoln explained. "The Congress can make laws for the whole Union. The Union is bigger than any state. Because the Union is all the states put together. If Congress makes a law, all the states have to obey it."

"What if they don't want to?" Willie asked. "Can they get out of the Union?"

Robert looked up from his booklet.

"Now you're talking about secession, Willie," he said.

"I am?" The little boy looked pleased. "Golly, I never even heard the word before. What does it mean?"

"It means leaving the Union," his big brother told him. "We had a debate at school. 'Has a state the right to secede from the Union?' I was on the side that said it hadn't. We won, too."

A frown crossed Mary Lincoln's pretty face. The word *secession* was often in the air these days. Even the school children were talking of it. All this discussion made her head ache.

"Bedtime, children," she said briskly. "Run along, now."

When they had gone she turned to her husband. "You look tired out, Mr. Lincoln. Better get to bed yourself."

[*127*]

"I reckon you're right." Wearily Lincoln dragged himself out of the rocking chair. "This is going to be a hard campaign, Mary. There won't be much sleep for me between now and Election Day."

The Lincoln-Douglas debates were arranged and went on all summer. Both men

[128]

made the best speeches they had ever made. Douglas argued that any new state wanting slavery should have it. Lincoln argued that the evil of slavery should not be allowed to spread.

At last Election Day came. When the votes were counted, they showed that Lincoln had lost. Stephen A. Douglas was re-elected Senator from Illinois.

But no election could settle the slavery question. All over the country, the trouble grew. The Southern states were talking openly of secession. If the United States Government interfered with slavery, they said, they would leave the Union.

Abraham Lincoln had not yet made up his mind how slavery could be ended. But he felt very sure of one thing. Whatever happened, the Union must hold together.

Many thoughtful men felt as he did. They asked Lincoln to come and talk to the people in their states. He made trips to the Middle West, to New York and New England. He begged his listeners to forget about their states and think about the whole country. They were all Americans. They must not let the United States of America be broken up.

Lincoln's thoughtful speeches made him a famous man. In 1860, the Republican party nominated him for President.

His opponent was again Senator Douglas. And this time, it was Lincoln who won. In November, 1860, Abraham Lincoln was elected President of the United States.

CHAPTER TWELVE

On to the White House

THE DAY after Election Day was an exciting one. Lincoln was downtown all day, greeting the friends who came to congratulate him. It was late at night when he came home. The children should have been in bed. But instead, Willie and Tad met him at the door.

"Mama's not home," they told him. "Some ladies are giving a party for her. Maria said we could stay up until you came. Come and see what we've been doing, Papa."

They dragged him into the living room. A big carpetbag stood in the middle of the floor.

It was filled with the boys' toys. Their spare
clothing was scattered over the chairs.

"We're packing up," Willie explained.
"We got all the toys in first. Now there's no
room for our clothes. I wanted Tad to leave
his drum behind—look how it fills up the bag!

But he says he won't go without his drum. What'll we do, Papa?"

Lincoln laughed. "We'll find a place for the drum when the time comes," he said. "You don't need to do your packing yet, boys. We won't be leaving for Washington until March."

The boys stared at him.

"But you got elected yesterday," Willie said. "You're the President now. I thought we'd move into the White House right away."

"Then you thought wrong, my boy," Lincoln answered. "I won't become the President until I'm inaugurated in March. So you see it'll be about three months before we go to Washington."

Before the boys could speak, they heard their mother's voice. Mrs. Lincoln came in, looking very pretty in her velvet bonnet and cloak.

"What's all this?" she asked. "Are you children still up? Really, I'll have to scold Maria."

[*133*]

"Mama," Willie said, "did you know we're not going to Washington until March? How can we wait that long?"

"The time will pass," she said cheerfully. "Now gather up the things you have scattered around here. That's my good boys. And up-stairs to bed with you."

When the boys had gone, Mrs. Lincoln smiled at her husband.

"Three months is a long time to wait, at their ages," she said. "For me, it's going to be short. I'll have to see to new clothes for all of us. I suppose you'll be busy too."

"Yes, there's a great deal to do," Lincoln agreed. "I'll have to wind up my law practice. Then I must begin planning my Cabinet. It's very important to choose the right men, and find out if they'll serve. And if I have time, I want to go down and say good-by to my step-mother. I owe a lot to her."

"Yes, and she must be very proud of you now." Mrs. Lincoln looked at the clock.

"Heavens, it's late! You must get some rest."

Abraham Lincoln got little rest in the months before his inauguration. Newspaper men from all over the country came for interviews. Politicians sought him out to ask for jobs in the new administration. There were letters to write, people to see, and speeches to make. It was not until January that he found time to visit his stepmother.

Lincoln's father had died ten years before. Old Mrs. Lincoln lived alone with her son Johnny Johnston. Johnny met Lincoln at the railroad station with a sleigh. It was a crisp winter day. The fields were covered with sparkling snow.

The jingle of sleigh bells brought Sarah Lincoln to her door. She had dressed in her Sunday best, with a white lawn cap tied under her chin. Lincoln jumped down from the sleigh and gave her a big hug.

"Come on in to the fire, son," she said.

She led the way indoors. By the glowing

stove she helped Abe off with his coat. He had
wound a little wool shawl high around his
throat. Now, as he pulled it off, his stepmother
stared.

"Land sakes, Abe, you got whiskers!" she
exclaimed. "I declare, if they hadn't been
covered up I'd never 'a' known you. Changes
your whole face."

Abe laughed. "Changes it for the better, I
hope. At least, that's why I grew 'em.

"I had a letter from a little girl up in New
York State. She felt sorry for me because I'm so
homely. She said if I'd grow a beard, I'd have
a better chance of getting elected. I took her
advice, and by jingo, I *did* get elected! So I
reckon the whiskers are here to stay. I hope
you like them."

"I'm not sure." Mrs. Lincoln studied the
long, dark face crowned with its shock of
coarse black hair.

She had not seen much of her stepson since
he had left home. Every time they met, she was

distressed by how much older he looked. There were deep furrows in his cheeks. He was as tall as ever, but his shoulders were growing bent. Well, that was to be expected, she thought. Abe wasn't a boy any more.

"Sit down, Abe." She pulled a chair close to the stove, and took another one near him. "How is Mary?"

"Mary's fine," he answered. "She's off on a shopping spree. Says she hasn't a dress fit to wear to Washington. Tell me about yourself, Ma. Is the rheumatism any better?"

"Oh, it comes and goes," she said cheerfully. "As long as I can keep on my feet, I don't complain. We had a letter from Sairey the other day, Abe. Seems like her and Dennis are doing real well out in Missouri. And Tildy has another baby. I guess that's all the family news. Now let's talk about you. How does it feel?"

"How does what feel?" Abe tilted back to put his feet comfortably on the wood box.

[137]

"To be President, of course. Oh, I know you ain't started on the job yet. But you've had a couple of months to get used to the notion. So how do you feel now?"

Lincoln glanced around the quiet room. His eyes met the kindly old eyes fixed on his face. "I'll tell you, Ma," he said abruptly. "Wouldn't whisper it to anybody else, but you always get the truth out of me. I'm scared to death."

"Scared? Scared of what?"

"Of the job," he answered soberly. "No President ever had a job like this one, Ma. Oh, I don't suppose it's ever been easy. It wasn't easy even for George Washington. But Ma, look. Washington and the other Presidents had a united country behind them. Nobody was trying to split the nation in two. There was no danger of the Union being broken up.

"Well, that's my trouble, Ma. I've *got* to hold the Union together, whatever it costs! If I fail—"

He broke off and buried his face in his hands. The old lady watched him helplessly.

"Folks around here say all this secession

talk won't come to anything," she ventured.

"Not come to anything?" He raised his head. "Do you know what's happened this very month? South Carolina voted before Christmas to secede. Since then, five Southern states have done the same. They've called a convention. They say they're going to start a new nation. They'll elect their own President. It means the end of the United States."

"But they can't do that!" Mrs. Lincoln said indignantly. "You'll be the President soon, Abe. You can't let them bust up the Union."

He looked straight at her. "And how am I to stop it? By war?"

The old lady shuddered. "Good gracious, no! Wars are against foreigners. Like the British or the Mexicans. Or even the Indians. But you don't have a war with your own people. Why, you'd have kinfolks a-killing each other! It's too horrible to think of," she exclaimed.

"Yet I must think of it," Lincoln said sadly. "Do you wonder I can't sleep of nights?"

Mrs. Lincoln laid a tender hand on his bowed shoulder.

"It's a heavy load you're called on to carry, son," she said gently. "If it's too much for you, remember there's always One ready to lend a helping hand. Take it to the Lord in prayer, Abe."

"Don't know as the Lord pays much attention to a politician's prayers, Ma." Abe tried to laugh. "I'd feel safer with my case in your hands. You pray for me while I'm in Washington. And keep on praying, will you? If I never needed your prayers before, I sure enough need them now."

Lincoln spent the afternoon with his stepmother, and ate the delicious supper she cooked for him. Then he went back to Springfield and all the work that waited for him there.

At last the day of departure came. The little boys were dancing with excitement. This was the first long trip they had ever taken. And at the end of it, there would be the White House!

The Springfield railway station was crowded with friends and neighbors. Lincoln sadly made a speech of farewell. The train moved off. Abraham Lincoln was about to begin his duties as President. Before him, as he had said in his farewell speech, lay a task "greater than that which rested upon Washington."

CHAPTER THIRTEEN

"This Means War!"

E XCUSE us, sir. Let us through, please."

Willie and Tad wriggled through the crowd as politely as they could.

There was always a crowd in the hall outside the President's White House office. All day long, men came to ask favors. Some wanted to be appointed postmaster in their home towns. Others wanted jobs here in Washington. Lincoln thought it was his duty to see them all.

"Come on, Tad." Willie dodged around a fat man and reached the office door.

"Who are those children?" the fat man asked the guard.

"They're Mr. Lincoln's little boys," the guard answered. "He gives them the run of the White House. All right, young gentlemen. Go on in."

He opened the door a crack, and the boys squeezed through.

"Papa!" Willie shouted. "We know where we can get a goat. Will you buy us a goat, Papa?"

"He pulls a cart," Tad put in. "We want the cart too. Please, Papa!"

They had reached their father's desk. The President was not alone. Several gentlemen were seated in chairs facing him. Their faces were very grave. Now they looked impatiently at the two little boys.

However, Abraham Lincoln gave the children his usual smile. "I'm pretty busy right now, boys," he said. "Suppose you wait right over there in the corner. I'll talk to you pretty soon."

"Yes, Papa." Willie and Tad found a corner by the bookcase. They sat down cross-legged on the carpet. The gentlemen went on with their conversation.

The boys had often been present while the President talked to visitors. Usually the talk was all the same. The visitor wanted an appointment to some job.

But this time it was different. Over and over came a word new to Tad—"Fort Sumter."

"What's that?" Tad whispered to his brother. "What's a fortsumter?"

"It's a fort on an island that belongs to South Carolina," Willie whispered back. "Papa was telling Mama about it last night. The Confederates are trying to take it away from our soldiers."

"Confederates are the Southerners, aren't they?" Tad said. "The ones that want to split up the country? Well, they can't take our forts away from us. Papa won't have that."

"Hush!" Willie stopped him. "Listen to what Papa's saying."

[145]

Lincoln had risen to his feet. "This means war, gentlemen," he said sorrowfully.

"But, Mr. President—" one of the men began.

"We have no choice," Lincoln answered. "The Confederates have struck the first blow. When they captured Fort Sumter, it was an act of war. They hauled down the Stars and Stripes and ran up the Confederate flag."

The President's voice grew very solemn.

"Sirs," he said, "the United States is now at war. Our struggle is against those Americans who call themselves Confederates. God help us all!"

The visitors had little to say. Slowly they filed out. Lincoln sat down again. He bent over his desk until his head rested on his arms.

Willie looked at Tad. Something told them this was no time to ask for a goat. Timidly the little boys approached their father.

"Don't you feel good, Papa?" Tad asked. "Maybe we'd better not bother you now."

Lincoln raised his head. "You are never a bother, my sons," he said tenderly. "But you find me in deep trouble. Nothing but war will save the Union. And war it must be!"

The little boys looked at each other uncertainly. Before they could speak, the door opened.

"Mr. President!" the guard called. "General Winfield Scott is here. He says you sent for him."

"Show him in." Lincoln rose and came forward, as General Scott entered the room.

"This is a bad business, General," said Lincoln, as he shook hands. "We must decide what is best to do."

The peppery old general scowled at the children. Scott had won glory in the Mexican War. Now he was old and sick, but very stiff and proud still. He wore a handsome uniform and a gold-mounted sword.

Willie met the general's frowning glance. "I guess we'd better go, Papa," he said hastily.

[147]

"Mama said not to be late for supper again."

The boys scuttled out. For once the hallway was empty. The guard had sent all the visitors away. Mr. Lincoln had no time for small matters now.

The war between the North and the South had begun.

In the beginning, the Southerners won most of the battles. The first big Union victory did not come until the war was nearly a year old. A young captain from the War Office brought news of this victory to the White House. It was midnight. The messenger had expected to find everyone asleep. But lights still burned in the mansion's upper story.

"The President—I must see the President!" he said breathlessly.

The old servant who had opened the door, shook his head.

"Ain't no seeing the President tonight, sir. Him and the Missus is a-watching over little Master Willie. The child is powerful sick of a fever. His pappy won't leave him."

"Then I'll go up to the sickroom." The captain pushed past the old man. "I have news that won't wait."

He climbed the stairs to the boys' room. The door was closed. At the captain's knock, a doctor came to open it.

[*149*]

"Go away," he whispered. "The boy is very low. The President will see nobody tonight."

"He *must* see me, Doctor," the messenger answered urgently. "A dispatch has just come through from Tennessee. The Confederates have surrendered Fort Donelson. I've got General Grant's telegram here."

"Wait a minute." The doctor turned back into the room, leaving the door open behind him.

The messenger could see little Tad, asleep in his own bed. Mrs. Lincoln slept too, napping on a sofa. But on the second bed the older boy tossed restlessly, muttering in delirium. And beside the bed Abraham Lincoln sat, arms folded, sleeplessly watching.

The doctor tiptoed up and whispered in his ear. Lincoln rose and came forward. He stepped into the hall and shut the door. His eyes were sunken, his gaunt face set in lines of suffering.

"Well?" he demanded. "You have a telegram from Tennessee? Let's have it. I can't spare much time."

The officer handed him the yellow slip. Lincoln's weary face lightened as he read.

"Fort Donelson, eh? The Confederates'

stronghold on the Tennessee River. This means that the way to Nashville lies open. You're right, my boy. This *is* good news!"

"And *unconditional* surrender, too—did

you see that?" the young captain asked eagerly. "I tell you, Mr. President, this man Grant knows his business. They wanted to talk terms with him. No terms, says Grant. Unconditional surrender, that's what. Who is this General Grant, anyway? I never heard of him before. But he sounds like the kind of general we need in this war!"

"General Ulysses S. Grant—General Unconditional Surrender Grant, I guess we'll be calling him now," Lincoln answered.

For the moment, the good news had cheered him. His voice grew stronger.

"Grant's an Illinois man like me, but I don't know him either. He was at West Point, but he'd been out of the army for years when this war broke out. Came back in as a volunteer. Reckon you're right, Captain. He certainly sounds like the kind of general we've been looking for."

The Fort Donelson victory gave new heart to the North. Washington celebrated it with parades and fireworks. For most people in the capital city, this was a time of rejoicing.

For the Lincolns, it was a time of sorrow. Even little Tad kept away from the celebration. Willie Lincoln died four days after Fort Donelson fell. He was twelve years old.

The evening of the funeral, Lincoln went to Tad's room. The younger boy had wept himself into a fever.

Lincoln sat down beside his bed. At his father's gentle voice, Tad began to sob again. Lincoln took the boy in his arms to comfort him.

"There, there, sonny," he soothed. "Hush your crying now and listen to your pappy. Right this minute, other boys' brothers are dying on the battlefields. Their folks have to pick up and go on, and be as brave as they can. You and Willie were always brave boys, Tad. He'd expect you to be brave now."

"I know it." Tad gulped and wiped his eyes. "I'll try, Papa. I'll be as brave as I can."

"That's my boy." Lincoln forced his own sad face into a smile.

"Now I've been thinking, Tad," he went on. "It'll be pretty lonesome for us with Willie gone. We'll have to keep each other company more. You know how I'm always having to ride out to the army camp on the Potomac River? Well, now. Suppose we get you a pony. Then you can ride along with me."

"A real pony horse? Golly, Papa!" Tad's voice rose. "Course, I've already got the goat. But you can't go far in a goat cart. Would Mama let me ride all the way to camp on the pony horse?"

"We'll fix it so she'll have to," Lincoln answered. "You know the President is Commander in Chief of the Army. Well, I'll appoint you my aide-de-camp. Nobody can stop you from going then."

"Yes, sir!" Tad sprang to the floor. In his long white nightgown he drew himself up. His hand went to his forehead in salute.

"Lieutenant Lincoln reporting for duty, sir!" he said in his deepest voice.

For the first time since Willie fell ill, father and son laughed together.

CHAPTER FOURTEEN

The President Speaks

Tad was waiting for his father to finish speaking with his last visitor. This was an old lady whose soldier son was in the guardhouse. From what Tad could make out, the soldier had gone home without leave.

"My boy done it for me, Mr. Lincoln," the old mother sobbed. "He heard I was sick. He knowed there was nobody to cut me some firewood and milk the cow. He had to come home and help me. Now they call him a deserter. He didn't aim to desert. He only come home to help his mammy. Please, please—"

Lincoln had listened patiently. Now he

patted the visitor's arm. "There, there, you don't have to plead with me. I'll get your son off this time. But remember, it mustn't happen again. Now dry your eyes and run along."

Weeping now from joy, the old lady hurried out. Tad jumped up as the door closed behind her. But Lincoln had turned back to his desk. He took a paper from a drawer and was studying it carefully.

Tad came over to him.

"Aren't you ready to go now, Papa?" he asked. "You promised to take me out to the soldier camp for supper. A real supper cooked over a campfire! It'll be too late if we don't start soon."

"Just a minute, Tad," Lincoln answered. His eyes were still on the paper. ". . . Are, and henceforward shall be, free," he read aloud.

Tad caught the last word. "Free? Is that about the slaves, Papa? Are you going to set them free now?"

Lincoln sighed. "I can't do it now, Tad. Saying a thing doesn't make it so. You may call a calf's tail a leg, but that doesn't give the calf five legs. I can say the slaves must be free. But it is the South that has slaves. The Southerners won't free their slaves because I say so."

Tad looked puzzled. "But you do say so, Papa. You've written it on that paper."

"This paper is my Emancipation Proclamation," Lincoln explained. "I'm keeping it until our army has a big victory. Then I'll proclaim to the whole world that we mean to make America a free country for everyone."

The President folded the paper and put it back in the drawer.

"Don't say a word about this, Tad," he said. "My Cabinet knows about it, and a few other people. You must help us keep it a secret until the right time comes."

The right time came in September of 1862. The Union won a bloody battle at Antietam Creek. Lincoln hurried out to the camp. He thanked General McClellan and all his brave soldiers, who had won the victory. Then the President immediately gave his Proclamation to the newspapers. It was to take effect on January 1, 1863. Since that day, all American men, women, and children, whatever their color, have been free.

The next important Union victory came at Gettysburg, in Pennsylvania. Nearly three thousand Union soldiers bought that victory with their lives.

A few months after the battle, it was decided to make a national cemetery of the bat-

tlefield. The dedication took place in November. The principal speaker was to be Mr. Edward Everett, former Governor of Massachu-

setts. Lincoln had promised to attend and to say a few words.

Lincoln and several members of his Cabinet went to Gettysburg on a special train. The night before the ceremony, Lincoln sat up late writing the speech he would deliver. He took it to one of his Cabinet members.

"Look it over and tell me what you think of it," he said. "I just can't seem to get my mind on it. I'm tired tonight, and I'm worried about my boy Tad. He was sick in bed with a feverish cold when I left home. Does the speech read all right to you?"

His friend looked it over. "It sounds fine, but it's pretty short," he remarked.

"Well, maybe I can add a few lines in the morning." Lincoln stretched and yawned. "I'm just about worn out. I'll try to get some sleep now."

In the morning things looked brighter. A telegram had arrived from the White House. Mrs. Lincoln wired that Tad was much better.

The doctor said he would be up in a day or two.

With a lighter heart, Lincoln looked over his speech and made a few changes. It still did not satisfy him. But there was no time to add to it now. The parade to the cemetery was forming. Outside he could hear the tramp of marching feet, and the notes of a bugle.

He dressed carefully in his best black suit, his white gloves and tall silk hat. A horse had been provided for him to ride. At the head of the procession, President Lincoln rode out to Gettysburg National Cemetery.

The platform was crowded with important people. Lincoln took his place among them. He listened to the hymns, the prayers, the introductory speeches. Then he settled back on his hard bench as portly Mr. Edward Everett rose.

Mr. Everett talked for exactly two hours. No one could say it was not a very fine speech. He finished at last to a round of applause. He

From his pocket he brought out a crumpled paper

bowed graciously and sat down, highly pleased with himself.

President Lincoln was introduced. He fumbled with his glasses. From his pocket he brought out a crumpled paper. He began to read. And in less than five minutes he put the paper back in his pocket and sat down. His speech was over.

At first the people were too startled to applaud. Could that be all? Yes, it must be, for the speakers were getting up to go. There was a little hasty hand clapping. No one there dreamed that he had just heard one of the greatest speeches of all time, the famous Gettysburg Address.

The Gettysburg Address

ourscore and seven years ago, our fathers brought forth on this continent a new nation, conceived in liberty, and dedicated to the proposition that all men are created equal.

"Now we are engaged in a great civil war testing whether that nation, or any nation so conceived and so dedicated, can long endure. We are met on a great battlefield of that war. We have come to dedicate a portion of that field as a final resting place for those who here gave their lives that that nation might live. It is altogether fitting and proper that we should do this.

"But, in a larger sense, we cannot dedicate, we cannot consecrate, we cannot *hallow this ground. The brave men, living and dead, who struggled here have consecrated it far above our poor power to add or detract. The world will little note nor long remember what we say here, but it can never forget what they did here. It is for us, the living, rather, to be dedicated here to the unfinished work which they who fought here have thus far so nobly advanced. It is rather for us to be here dedicated to the great task remaining before us — that from these honored dead we take increased devotion to that cause for which they gave the last full measure of devotion — that we here highly resolve that these dead shall not have died in vain; that this nation, under God, shall have a new birth of freedom; and that government of the people, by the people, for the people, shall not perish from the earth."*

CHAPTER FIFTEEN

The Last Day

THE GUARD opened the study door.

"General Grant's messenger to see you, Mr. President," he announced.

A young officer, very handsome in his smart uniform, came quickly into the room.

"Captain Robert Lincoln, sir," he said. "Reporting from General Grant. The general will be with you for the Cabinet meeting at eleven o'clock."

Lincoln swept his papers aside. He stared, and stared again. Then he jumped up and grasped the young man's hand.

"Bob! This is a surprise. I didn't know

Grant was bringing you to Washington with him. Does your mother know you're here?"

"Not yet," Robert Lincoln answered. "I came straight from the station. General Grant

is over at the War Office. He told me to come on ahead. I have only a short leave. We're pretty busy down at headquarters. Winding up a war is a big job."

"Yes, but it's a pleasant job," Lincoln said. "I still can't get used to it. It's been five days now since General Lee surrendered. Washington has done nothing but celebrate all week. Your brother Tad is just about crazy with all the excitement."

"I can imagine so." Robert Lincoln smiled. "I'll have a chance to get acquainted with my little brother now. I've hardly seen him at all since you came to Washington. I was away at college all those years, and lately I've been in the army. Well, the war's over now. I'll be back in the family again."

"Your mother will be glad of that," Lincoln answered. "You'd better run along and see her now. I'll be with you for lunch."

Robert left, and a little later the Cabinet gathered for the meeting. General Grant was present as a guest. He described General Lee's surrender, and spoke of his Confederate prisoners.

"I'm sending them home as fast as I can,"

the general said. "That is what you want, Mr. President, isn't it?"

Lincoln nodded. "If you're quick about it, General, they'll be back on their farms for the spring plowing. I'm glad you allowed them to keep their horses, too. They'll need them on the farms. We want to be easy on these fellows. They fought on the losing side. But they fought bravely and well. It's not for us to punish them. We won, and they lost. Now we'll put the whole sorry business behind us, and all be Americans again."

The meeting broke up, and Lincoln went to join his family at luncheon. Just at noon there came a boom of cannon. Tad jumped up.

"What's that?" he asked. "Has the war started again?"

His big brother laughed. "No, Tad, the war is over for good. The noise you hear is a salute. It was four years ago today that the war started. Now our soldiers are celebrating because it is

[171]

ended. They're firing salutes in all the Union army camps."

"I wish they would find some other way to celebrate," Mrs. Lincoln said. "I've heard

enough cannonfire to last me for a lifetime. Let's talk about something besides war for a change. Mr. Lincoln, don't forget you're taking me to the theater tonight. They say Miss

[*172*]

Laura Keene is very comical in her new play. It's time we had something to laugh at again."

They sat long over their meal, a loving, united family. It was a beautiful spring day, with lilacs in bloom outside the open window.

Mary Lincoln looked happily around her, at her handsome soldier son, at the eager younger one, and at her husband. She had not seen him so full of smiles and jokes for many a weary year. The war was over. Hearts could be glad again.

That afternoon, Mr. and Mrs. Lincoln went for a drive in the spring sunshine. They chatted joyfully of the future. When his term ended, Lincoln declared, they would go home to Illinois. There, in their little white house, among dearly loved friends, they would pass their lives in peace and quiet.

After supper the President and his wife left for the theater. The Presidential box was draped in flags. The play had already begun when the Lincolns entered the theater. But the orchestra struck up *Hail to the Chief.* The crowd rose and cheered.

Mary Lincoln, in a new gown of violet silk and lace, stood at the rail and bowed graciously. The President smiled and waved and waved again. Some of the audience had never before seen that tired, worn face break into smiles. They said afterward they were glad they could remember him as a happy man.

Mrs. Lincoln took her seat. Her husband sat beside her, in a big rocking chair brought in especially for his comfort. The music changed to a popular waltz. The play went on.

It was a comedy called "Our American Cousin." It was very funny. Lincoln laughed and clapped with the rest of the audience. When the first act ended he chatted with his wife and the young couple who were their guests. The curtain rose for the second act.

In a passage behind the President's box, a pale young man crouched with a pistol in his hand. He was a half-crazy actor named John

[*174*]

Wilkes Booth. Booth was a Southerner. He hated Lincoln with an insane hatred. He had sworn revenge for the South's defeat.

The second act began. Noiselessly, John

Wilkes Booth stepped into the box. Stealthily he crept behind Lincoln's chair. He raised his pistol and fired. Then he leaped to the stage. With a wild shout he pushed past the terrified actors and disappeared through a back door.

Lincoln slumped down in his chair. A doctor hurried up from the audience. The unconscious President was carried to the nearest house and laid upon a bed. More doctors came. The Cabinet was summoned. Robert Lincoln came to comfort his grief-stricken mother. But in his bed at the White House, little Tad slept peacefully. He did not know that he would never hear his father's tender voice again.

Lincoln lived through the night. He died with the coming of daybreak. He died, but the Union he had saved lives on. And while it lives, while free men cherish freedom, the spirit of Abraham Lincoln will never die.

"Names That Made History"

ENID LAMONTE MEADOWCROFT, *Supervising Editor*

THE STORY OF ANDREW JACKSON
By Enid LaMonte Meadowcroft.   *Illustrated by David Hendrickson*

THE STORY OF JOAN OF ARC
By Jeannette Covert Nolan.   *Illustrated by Pranas Lapé*

THE STORY OF JOHN PAUL JONES
By Iris Vinton.   *Illustrated by Edward A. Wilson*

THE STORY OF LAFAYETTE
By Hazel Wilson.   *Illustrated by Edy Legrand*

THE STORY OF ROBERT E. LEE
By Iris Vinton.   *Illustrated by John Alan Maxwell*

THE STORY OF ABRAHAM LINCOLN
By Nina Brown Baker.   *Illustrated by Warren Baumgartner*

THE STORY OF MOZART
By Helen L. Kaufmann.   *Illustrated by Eric M. Simon*

THE STORY OF FLORENCE NIGHTINGALE
By Margaret Leighton.   *Illustrated by Corinne B. Dillon*

THE STORY OF LOUIS PASTEUR
By Alida Sims Malkus.   *Illustrated by Jo Spier*

THE STORY OF POCAHONTAS
By Shirley Graham.   *Illustrated by Mario Cooper*

THE STORY OF MARCO POLO
By Olive Price.   *Illustrated by Federico Castellon*

THE STORY OF THEODORE ROOSEVELT
By Winthrop Neilson.   *Illustrated by Edward A. Wilson*

THE STORY OF MARK TWAIN
By Joan Howard.   *Illustrated by Donald McKay*

THE STORY OF GEORGE WASHINGTON
By Enid LaMonte Meadowcroft.   *Illustrated by Edward A. Wilson*

THE STORY OF MARTHA WASHINGTON
By Jeannette Covert Nolan.   *Illustrated by Corinne B. Dillon*

THE STORY OF MAD ANTHONY WAYNE
By Hazel Wilson.   *Illustrated by Lawrence Beall Smith*

1 Born in Hodgenville, Kentucky, February 12, 1809

2 Moves to Springfield, Illinois, to practice law, 1837

3 Meets his future wife, Mary Todd, 1839

4 Takes part in the Lincoln-Douglas Debates, 1858

10 Shot by John Wilkes Booth, Lincoln dies April 15, 1865

9 Told of Lee's surrender, ending the Civil War, 1865